KATERI

OF THE

MOHAWKS

By

Marie Cecilia Buehrle

THE BRUCE PUBLISHING COMPANY
MILWAUKEE

NIHIL OBSTAT:

John A. Schulien, S.T.D.
Censor librorum

IMPRIMATUR:

✠ Albertus G. Meyer
Archiepiscopus Milwauchiensis

Die 8ª Februarii, 1954

To Doctor Edmund J. Rhodebeck,

whose enthusiasm inspired the writing of this book,
whose scholarship helped to fashion it,
whose love for Kateri
is its life.

The author offers grateful acknowledgment to Rev. Henri Béchard, S.J., and Rev. Thomas J. Coffey, S.J., vice postulators respectively for Canada and the United States; to Rev. Thomas Grassmann of the Kateri Tekakwitha museum at Fonda, N. Y.; to the Rev. George Brodeur, S.J., pastor of the Mission of St. Francis Xavier at Caughnawaga; and to the Montour family, with whom the author lived during her stay at the Iroquois village. For source material she is indebted to the "Positio of the Historical Section of the Sacred Congregation of Rites," which contains the life story of Kateri as submitted to Rome; to Ellen Walworth's *The Lily of the Mohawks*; and to the *Jesuit Relations*.

INTRODUCTION

by

Edmund J. Rhodebeck, M.D., Fellow N. Y. Acad. Med.*

Surely another life of Kateri Tekakwitha must seem unnecessary. Everything that is known about her has been written many times and in several languages, and the size of her bibliography is astounding. All that is known for certain can be found in the accounts by Fathers Cholenec and Chauchetière, her confessor and her spiritual director. Additional details are presented in the recently published "Positio of the Historical Section of the Sacred Congregation of Rites." That is all that there is.

I met Kateri a few years ago when a casual acquaintance presented me with a medal of a little Indian girl, a Mohawk of the Iroquois tribe in which I had always been interested. Immediately I sensed what newspapermen would call a human interest story when the facts of her life were told to me. How could a Mohawk girl of that age and cultural pattern tread the path that Kateri trod? What made her do so? What factors in her life played parts in the formation of her personality? What was her personality pattern? What was her cultural setting?

* Author's Note: Dr. Rhodebeck worked in collaboration with me on Kateri of the Mohawks. He is really the moving spirit behind this book. For some time he had been doing research work on the Indians of the Five Nations and especially on Kateri. Dr. Rhodebeck, a recent convert, died September 28, 1952 in New Orleans.

Kateri was the first saintly person in whom I really became interested. The accounts of the lives of others which I had read were such that I had very little in common with them. They were not human. They needed "defrosting" and I should not want that to happen to Kateri. I should not want her gilded up and surrounded by an aura in which the struggles and strivings of a little Indian girl, and a not too happy one, played no part.

Here was an Indian child, orphaned, physically handicapped, who followed an adaptive pattern of life which seemingly led her insensibly to the end which she attained. One can see a gradual tilling of the soil, a refining of it, until the coming of the Jesuits and their doctrine of the Incarnation and the Redemption planted a seed which ripened with great rapidity and burst forth into an expression of all her repressed desires. Here was an answer to her struggles, her strivings, her unhappiness. She found One whom she could love and trust without fear.

Now comes the question of how to approach such a problem. How is it possible to make Kateri come to life? How portray her as a girl and woman growing in sanctity and not as a saint who was secondarily a woman? How show that her handicaps were used as steppingstones for the achievement of this purpose? How demonstrate also that God works best through His use of natural means and thus makes these things more comprehensible to us who are human beings with only human understanding? How enable us to say when we have known and understood: "There by the grace of God and with my co-operation, I may go"?

Unfortunately so little is known of the cultural pattern of the Iroquois at the time at which Kateri lived that it is very difficult to place her in her natural setting. Indeed no

one in speaking or writing of their contacts with the Iroquois
has given a descriptive account of their lives and ways of life
or of their home life and of the little intimate things which
make up human relationships. All we have are a few brief
passages in the Jesuit Relations. We do, however, know
enough of Iroquois life and occupations to know the limita-
tions which would be imposed upon a person with Kateri's
handicaps.

Unlike the Algonquin tribes by whom they were surrounded, the Iroquois were town builders. Instead of wander-
ing from place to place to hunt, they preferred fixed abodes,
houses enclosed in a compound walled by a double or triple
palisade outside of which were fields where they could raise
their corn. They were distinctly agrarian and depended more
on agriculture than on hunting, for their staple food supply.

The Mohawks, the tribe to which Kateri belonged, were
the easternmost tribe of the Iroquois Federation and they
built their towns on undulating hills above the Mohawk
River, which flows eastward through a picturesque valley
and empties into the Hudson, not far above Albany.

Try to picture such a country covered with virgin forest.
Imagine a low hill, the top of which has been cleared and on
which an irregular rectangular, doubly palisaded town has
been built.

The Mohawk Castle of Gandawagué, where Kateri lived
most of her life, lies just on the limits of the present town of
Fonda, N. Y. The site of the old village is being excavated
by Father Thomas Grassmann, a Franciscan Conventual,
and a very scholarly priest, who has charge of Kateri's chapel
and museum just below the site of the village. Father Grassmann's work helps us to picture the setting in which Kateri
lived. After removal of the top soil, careful scraping of the

under soil reveals the posts, the double stockade, the outlines of the long houses, and those of the Council House. Round grayish patches in the earth show the positions of long vanished hearth fires, over one of which Kateri did her cooking.

The houses themselves were dome-shaped structures covered with bark and had a smoke vent in the roof and a door at the end. They were occupied by four or five families, each with its own hearth fire and a compartment in which the family lived, cooked, ate, worked, and slept. The lodges were dark, dingy, and very dirty.

Now in an enclosure of small size such as Gandawagué with palisaded walls averaging only 255 feet in length, community life must have been extremely close and intimate; hence any desire to stray from the common pattern of living or to do anything unusual must have been balked at the start. Ridicule and adverse criticism are great deterrents to individualistic tendencies.

Outside the enclosure, which was pierced by three or four small openings permitting ingress and egress, the ground was cleared for some distance, and the fields of maize and squash, which formed the staple foods of the community, were planted on the slope toward the Mohawk, and on the river bottom land. Since it was believed that woman possesses and controls the faculty of reproduction, it was she who had the sole care of the planting and cultivating, the harvesting and milling of the crop.

The tribal structure was definitely matriarchal, and the woman's position in the family was so important that it makes it difficult to understand why Kateri was so determined in her refusal to marry. Surely it must have been something very basic indeed, since virginity was completely at variance with the social pattern in which she lived. But fortunately for us and for her as it turned out, Kateri was not able to fit into the pattern adequately.

She had the disadvantage of being badly scarred, not pretty, with eyes severely damaged as a result of smallpox. Therefore she could not romp around in the sunlight or play as other children played. Also she was an orphan and had no understanding mother to whom she could turn and get help in her attempts at adaptation. A child under such conditions, having no brothers and sisters, has another handicap in the lack of close association with others of its own age group. It is forced, therefore, to make its adaptations in an adult environment. It is conscious of a void in its own life, all of which engenders a feeling of insecurity and consequent inferiority. Save for these things it is possible, even probable, that Kateri would have followed the normal pattern of Indian childhood and adolescence.

The Iroquoian women loved to adorn themselves. Kateri too, loved beautiful things; but what was the use of adornment to one who was scarred and not at all attractive? If she had been pretty, things might have been very different.

So for many reasons Kateri lived a life apart. I do not think that she was very happy. It is evident, however, that living more or less alone as she did, she would be occupied with thoughts wiser than the distractions of the average Indian girl who busied her mind with her work and play, with local gossip, and chatter about boy friends. Very early, Kateri had acquired an adult point of view, and this may account for Father de Lamberville's surprise at her quick grasp of the elements of Christianity later, when the telling hour was at hand.

It is evident, that day by day and trial by trial, the soil was being cultivated, and I certainly think that without such preparation Kateri would never have been ready as she was for the light when it came. It is another instance of God's grace acting through natural means to supply something that was badly needed at that time, an example for the new pagan converts to Christianity.

Now we come to Kateri's refusal to marry. Such a refusal was entirely out of character for a Mohawk girl of her time. Remember that the husband becomes one of the woman's family, another provider so to speak; so a good deal of pressure would be brought to bear upon her in order to force a marriage. Remember also that Kateri belonged to a childless family and from a social standpoint it was her moral duty to provide a helper for her aging uncle and aunt. One would think that her own insecurity would move her in that direction. But Kateri would have none of it. What she may have seen, heard, or experienced, we cannot ascertain; but whatever the cause, it constituted a threat to her which completely overbalanced any other consideration. Certainly she knew nothing of virginity at that time, nor of the idea of consecrating oneself to God. We do know that she had a real revulsion against the idea, for we have Father Cholenec who probably knew her better than anyone else, quoting Kateri as saying: "I hate marriage and am horrified at it."

What a safety device that was for a woman who was eventually to give herself to God! Her dislike of the very thought of marriage was so great that neither her own security nor her duty to her adopted parents could overcome it.

Here then was Kateri as she first came into contact with a Blackrobe, a shy, retiring girl, much of a recluse, much liked for her pleasant smile and for her desire to be helpful to everyone, a characteristic of those who, for one reason or another, need some protection. We find a girl not caring for the usual pleasures of women of her race, content with her needlework and the making of things for others, mature in her thinking, and certainly one who knew her own mind.

The process was slow and toilsome; but can anyone say that the soil had not been properly prepared? At any rate when Father de Lamberville came into contact with Kateri, he was aware, almost at once, that here was fertile ground. As for Kateri, the response was immediate and complete. A human being whose life, condemned by circumstances to loneliness, lovelessness, and unrest, had found at last that which she was so unconsciously seeking: One in whom she could find faith, One in whom she could find security, One whom she could love.

This is the secret of the Mohawk girl. This is the heart of Tekakwitha's story. It is a story that the human mind can understand and profit by. It is God's wondrous way of working through natural channels to form a person needed in her time and needed in the world of today. It is God's special gift to North America; for there lay the soil into which He planted the Lily of the Mohawks, Kateri Tekakwitha.

FOREWORD

As early as 1744, Father Francis Xavier de Charlevoix, S.J., called Venerable Kateri Tekakwitha the "New Star of the New World." Today Kateri is loved by thousands of American and Canadian devotees, so well loved, indeed, that the numerous worth-while biographies concerning her, have been bought up long ago. For several years, it had been impossible to procure a well-done book on the Lily of the Mohawks. To supply this need Miss Marie C. Buehrle, the author of *St. Maria Goretti,* a life of the Italian child martyr, has prepared KATERI OF THE MOHAWKS.

Keen psychology, patient research, and much love, along with its fluid English have made this book one of the most important published on this Indian servant of God. To all, but to Canadians especially, I warmly recommend KATERI OF THE MOHAWKS.

REV. HENRI BÉCHARD, S.J.
Canadian V. — Postulator for the Cause of Venerable Kateri Tekakwitha

FOREWORD

Marvelous is the word for the Lily of the Mohawks. Without, of course, anticipating the decisions of the Church as to the holiness of Venerable Kateri Tekakwitha, people call her today the "Sainted Savage," "Lily of New France," and hope with confidence that she will soon be called Blessed, then Saint.

Concrete evidence of the esteem in which Kateri is held by the official Church is the scene enacted in June, 1942, two hundred and eighty-six years after her birth at Ossernenon, now Auriesville, New York. The Sacred Congregation of Rites assembled at the Vatican. His Holiness, Pope Pius XII, presided from the Papal Throne. The Most Reverend Cardinal Relator rose to propose a question: *Has it been proved in this instance and for the purpose under consideration that the theological virtues, Faith, Hope, Love of God and of Neighbor, and the cardinal virtues, Prudence, Justice, Temperance, Fortitude and their subordinates, were of heroic degree?*

The Most Reverend Cardinals, official prelates, and Fathers Consultor gave their votes. His Holiness weighed their decision until the following January, that he might seek, through repeated prayer, greater light from God. The light came. Cardinal Salotti, Prefect of the Sacred Congregation, was summoned to the Pope's presence on January 3, 1943. With him was the Promotor General of the Faith. His Holiness offered the Holy Sacrifice of the Mass. And then he solemnly proclaimed: *It has been proved in this instance and for the purpose under consideration, that the theological virtues of Faith, Hope, Love of God and Neighbor, and the cardinal virtues, Prudence, Justice, Temperance, Fortitude and subordinate virtues of the Venerable Servant of God, Kateri Tekakwitha, were heroic.*

The subject of this narrative, had she been present at the formidable citation of her virtues, would surely have run from the room long before the Cardinals, let alone His Holiness, had finished. Miss Buehrle's authentic and moving biography of Kateri will do much to increase interest in the Lily of the Mohawks, move more of her clients to storm heaven for the required miracles, and hasten the time when, we hope and pray, we shall have, at long last, a *native* North American Saint.

May God speed the day!

> REV. THOMAS J. COFFEY, S.J.
> *Vice-Postulator for the United States of the Cause of Beatification and Canonization of Venerable Kateri Tekakwitha*

KATERI OF THE MOHAWKS

CHAPTER 1

Darkness lay heavily over the Valley of the Mohawks while the faint, swift dipping of paddles barely broke the stillness of the hour preceding the dawn. When the slow October light crept over the hills into the adjacent forest the sound ceased. A bird stirred in the thicket, a canoe slipped into concealment under the weeds, and the howl of a dog echoed over an empty river.

Along the trail winding like a tattered ribbon through the trees, three figures moved in single file. A Mohawk led the way, his head thrust forward, the scent of danger in his nostrils. From time to time his hands were outstretched, clearing the way, sheltering the girl behind him from the whip of a branch. Her step, light upon the fallen leaves, was swift as his. Her eyes were distended with fear and a tremor shook her at the slightest sound, the unexpected beat of a wing, the tap of a woodpecker, an uneasy shifting among the leaves. Behind her a Huron walked with slower pace, turning every few moments to watch for the approach of some terror from the rear.

Suddenly, something tore at the silence. The girl smothered a cry. The Mohawk stopped short, with fingers quick upon his musket; but he fired no shot. The Huron leaped up from behind. It was nothing but the whirr of a startled grouse.

No one spoke. The Mohawk's lips were drawn into a thinner line as the three fell into step again. The girl kept pace with the gathering speed. The brown shawl had dropped from her head and lay loosely about her shoulders; but she clutched it tightly at her throat. The path narrowed through the crowding trees. The Mohawk turned, his finger upon his lips.

"Kateri," he whispered, "stay close to Jacques. I must fall behind." Her eyes smiled in reply; but her lips did not move. He looked at the Huron, tapped his musket, and the Huron understood.

Not many miles away, at the Dutch trading post, Iowerano, the Turtle chief, rose abruptly, upsetting his mug of firewater, leaving his neighbors from Andagoron, the castle of the Bears, sitting at the table, staring and speechless. The conversation had become infuriating. For some time the mere mention of the Praying Castle on the St. Lawrence had been enough to put him into a rage, and now rumors were circulating in every corner of the Dutch town, that during his absence from the Turtle village of Gandawagué, the Oneida chief, the famous Hot Powder had come down from Canada with two other Christian Indians, and was speaking to the people. More and more these fanatics from the Praying Castle were luring the Christian Mohawks to Sault St. Louis. He shook his fist toward the north and without a word of explanation flung himself out of the low Dutch door, nearly colliding with Fleetfoot, the swiftest messenger of Gandawagué.

Chief Iowerano scowled. "Tell it quickly," he commanded before the other had a chance to speak. "Have the French come?"

"Tekakwitha," panted the messenger. "Tekakwitha has gone."

"Gone where?" roared the chief. "With whom?"

"No one knows. She is not in the long house. Hot Powder left yesterday for the castle of the Oneidas. This morning the Mohawk from the Sault and his companion, a Huron from Lorette, were missing."

Iowerano did not wait to hear more. "Tekakwitha has run away to Canada," he muttered to himself, suspicion giving way to a raging fear. In a hurry he provided himself with three bullets. "To kill," he growled as he picked up his musket and rushed from the trading post.

Shrewdly he estimated that the fugitives must have taken to the woods when they reached the sharp curve not far from the spot where Chuctamunda Creek tumbles downhill into the river. The forest was still as though stripped of every living thing. Not even a noiseless squirrel was scampering up a tree trunk. The leaves lay lightly scattered upon the ground as though no human foot had passed over them.

The trail curved. At last! Something was moving toward him. An Indian, but alone! Torn by the storm within him, Iowerano had not seen the Mohawk hesitate for a moment and then advance, knowing that it was too late to turn back without being discovered. He noticed only a nonchalant figure loitering along the way and looking about him; a hunter obviously, in search of game. Iowerano was not interested. He could not see the face of Onas and fury had dulled his usually keen perceptions. The man was standing still now, his back turned, looking up into a tree. The chief saw him point his gun and fire into the depths of the forest. Yes, a hunter. . . . Iowerano fingered his own musket and staggered on.

CHAPTER 2
It was the year 1656 in the village of Ossernenon on the south bank of the Mohawk River. In Chief Kenhoronkwa's lodge, Kahenta, the Algonquin wife, looked long and lovingly into the face of her sleeping papoose. At dawn when it was born, the women of the long house had gathered about her. The squaws of the village had come and gone. Nearly all the day her husband had been sitting near her by the fire, saying nothing, pulling meditatively at his pipe. He was a war chief; but no war paint slashed his face today. There was at least an interval of peace and the gentle Algonquin was glad.

Finally, without a word he slipped out of the cabin, and now for the first time Kahenta was alone. Timidly she glanced about the deserted long house. There was no sound but the hesitant crackling of the fire. She leaned over the child and it opened its eyes. She picked it up, wrapped the soft doeskin around it and rocked it in her arms, humming softly a poignant little tune to which gradually she found the words. It was Brébeuf's lullaby for the Christ Child, written for his Indian children at Christmas time long ago, when he had just come to the land of the Hurons.

"Within a lodge of broken bark
    The tender Babe was found;

6

> A ragged robe of rabbit skin
> Enwrapped His beauty round.
> And as the hunter braves drew nigh
> The Angels' song rang loud and high:
> 'Jesus, your King, is born; Jesus is born.
> In excelsis gloria.'"

Kahenta clasped her papoose more closely. Then more words came:

> "The earliest moon of winter time
> Is not so round and fair
> As was the ring of glory on
> The helpless infant there."

Kahenta's voice softened to a whisper. The child's eyes were closing.

> "While chiefs from far before Him knelt,
> With gifts of fox and beaver pelt" . . .

Kahenta's head bent lower. Her words trailed slowly into silence. The child was asleep.

A French woman had taught her the words of this song when she was a child. How she longed for her now! In this cruel pagan land to which she was a stranger, would her little girl ever learn as she had learned, to know and love Rawenniio, the white man's God? Would the Blackrobe ever come to the castle of the Turtles and baptize her? A look of terror crossed her face. If he did, the Mohawks would certainly kill him as they had killed Ondessonk, whom the French called Father Jogues. She remembered the morning well. It was when she was a little girl, only ten years ago, and the French woman's face had turned white as she told the harrowing story. It happened in this very village of Ossernenon and she wondered which was the long house that he was entering when the tomahawk struck him. Well could she visualize the scene of torture; for her own long house faced the square where the scaffold stood, and often, too often, she heard the cries of the captives and could do nothing but hide her head in her hands and pray. Had Kenhoronkwa, her husband, been one of Ondessonk's torturers? It was more than likely. She shuddered.

And yet she must not think unkindly of him. He had saved her from a captive's fate by making her his wife. As though it were yesterday she recalled the agonizing journey of the defeated Algonquins through forests and over lakes, along the war trail from the St. Lawrence into the Valley of the Mohawks, to her a dark and desolate country until today. The infant lay quietly upon her heart. The fire was burning low and the place was full of shadows. What would its future be? The child was a Mohawk — that, she must concede — but she was Algonquin, too. Since the Mohawks were a conquering tribe she would never, perhaps, be torn from all that she loved, as her mother had been. Only a few weeks ago the tragic story had repeated itself. The Iroquois had swept over the Isle of Orleans, destroyed the nation of the Hurons, and once more crowded the Turtle village with captives. Rumors had spread that the neighboring Onondagas were willing to make peace with Onnontio the French governor. Not so the Mohawks. They were continuing their raids upon the French frontier, and Kenhoronkwa was a war chief. He would have nothing to do with the French or the Blackrobes.

Again she remembered Father Jogues and trembled. She had been told about his mutilated hands and about the severed head placed high upon the palisade facing the

French frontier, the direction from which both he and she had come. "Ondessonk!" her heart cried out. "You came to save the Mohawks and they killed you. Here in our village they spilt your blood. Wash my little one with it; because the Blackrobe cannot come to pour the blessed water over her. Some day you will send him. Until then help me to give her a Christian heart. Be with me, Ondessonk!"

Deeply hidden within her thoughts, she was unaware of any sound until a sudden shaft of light told her that someone had withdrawn the heavy bearskin at the door. "Sago," said a vibrant voice that made Kahenta's soft eyes light with joy.

"Anastasia, come see!"

She tucked the sleeping baby in her lap more securely into the fur.

"Oonka Tee? — Who is this?" she whispered happily to it as her friend Anastasia Tegonhatsihongo bent over the child, took it into her lean, strong arms, and sat down beside the fire. Everything about her betokened energy and strength: her firm, quick step, the determined curve of her lips, the live-coal glow in her eyes. She was well advanced into middle age and had been a Christian for many years. With Mohawk courage she lived in her pagan surroundings unafraid and unhurt. To Kahenta the Algonquin, equally fervent, but mindful always of her character of rescued captive, she was a rock of security. Anastasia on her part loved Kahenta's quiet ways and the gracious manner that fitted more aptly to the French family that had sheltered her, than into the long house of the Iroquois.

"I have news, Kahenta."

The Algonquin raised questioning eyes. The women's voices were low. There was always the possibility of an unobserved listener in some corner of the lodge.

"A Blackrobe has come to our village," Anastasia continued. "The French call him Père Lemoyne; but he too has been given the name Ondessonk in memory of the martyred Jogues."

Kahenta held her breath.

"He has come," Anastasia said, "to bring comfort to the Huron exiles of the isle of Orleans. They are Christians."

"Oh! Anastasia," pleaded Kahenta, "do you think he would pour the blessed water over my little one?"

Slowly Anastasia shook her head.

"The Blackrobe has reproached the Mohawk warriors for cruelty. Your husband is not pleased. He will never permit him to come to you. He does not want his child to be a Christian."

"It is my fault," Kahenta said sadly. "He thinks me too fond of the French. He says that the white man has stolen the red man's land, has brought him only disease and made him drunk. What can I do, Anastasia, to make him change his mind?"

"You can pray, Kahenta, and you can be patient. Do not irritate him now. Who knows what may yet be in the castle of the Turtles? Remember that the Huron captives are Christians. On the Lake of Onondaga the Iroquois gather in St. Mary's Chapel and the Blackrobe preaches to them about the Christian laws of marriage. The women are deeply moved and want to learn Christianity. More Blackrobes have come since the Onondagas are at peace with the French."

"The Mohawks do not know peace." Kahenta's voice was piteous.

"Courage, Kahenta." Anastasia rose to go. "The squaw must learn to wait. She must know when to be silent."

"Who is this?
Who is this?
Giving eye-light
On the top of my lodge?"

Kahenta sang to her baby in the early morning while she
wrapped it up and strapped it to the carved and curtained
cradle board. She continued singing:

"It is I, the little owl,
Coming, coming.
It is I, the little owl,
Coming
Down! Down!"

She fastened it to her back, and went out of the shadowed
long house into the sunny morning. With the warm new
burden upon her, Kahenta no longer ached with the home-
sickness of Ruth "among the alien corn" as she looked out
over the billowing fields and toward the misty hills. These
no longer oppressed her as shutting her out forever from
the land that had been home to her. The slight tugging at
her shoulders gave them a strength unfelt before, and as she
hung her papoose onto the low-reaching branch of a maple
tree, she knew that here within this tiny compass, here was
home.

Joyously she stooped to her work, one of the many bent,
brown figures scattered among the yellow of the maize. The
breeze rocked her little bundle and whenever she looked up
it was swinging gently among the leaves and the birds were
singing merrily.

"Great Spirit," the heart of Kahenta prayed, "breathe upon
my little one that the poison may not touch her. Rawenniio,

lapped at the darkness. Sparks hissed about the frantic figures leaping into the air, twisting themselves into a dance of desperation. Rattles clapped a weird accompaniment to shrieks and moans of incantation. The people had offered victims to Manitou the spirit of evil, to Aireskoi the demon of war. They had feasted every oki that they knew; but the demon of pestilence would not be propitiated. Day after day, like falling leaves, more of the villagers were stricken. Night after night, with increasing despair the medicine man gathered herbs in the moonlight and caught the creatures of the darkness. With growing frenzy he and the sorcerers exercised their unavailing charms. Behind a grinning mask he was hiding his scarred face now, and glaring into the fire.

Higher and higher with the mounting flames the hunchbacked juggler leaped, beating the air, frothing at the mouth. With hilarity the Mohawk could whoop his way to war. Torture, he could both give and take. Bravely he could face the dangers of the forest, starvation amid trackless snows or when the blight lay upon the corn. These things he could understand; but here was mystery. Against this ravaging foe that made strong men die like sickened flies, he was helpless, and the terror of the unknown shook him to the soul.

A crowd, meantime, was jostling its way toward the long house of the chief. There was no more room within. Luridly, five fires smoldered in the fetid air. Braves with black-streaked faces, squaws sinking more deeply into their shawls, moved like grim shadows in the semidarkness. Hidden under pine branches heaped in a corner, the chief's dog howled. Kenhoronkwa lay stretched upon a beaver skin, clothed in deer hide, wearing new moccasins for the journey. His face was oiled. His narrow ridge of black hair worn in the fashion of the Mohawks, stood stiff and shining with bear grease.

Not far away in one of the alcoves floored with interlaced twigs of maple and oak, Kahenta, the chief's Algonquin wife, lay dying, with two dying children beside her. The smaller one, the boy, lay limply within the curve of her arm. The outgrown cradle board hung motionless from the rafter. The little girl, already four years old, clutched her corn-husk doll and tossed with fever. From a small bark bowl a middle aged woman with a gaunt, strong face, moistened Kahenta's forehead and the bluing lips of the child. The Algonquin opened her tired eyes: "Anastasia, the little ones are dying. Without the blessed water! I am praying, praying. Breath is leaving me; but the heart will pray until it stops. Anastasia bent lower. She rather felt than heard the word: "Rawenniio!"

Most probably Kahenta and even Anastasia did not know that a lay person could administer baptism. The visits of the missionary were infrequent at that period, and Christians among the Mohawks, few. It is more than likely that the Blackrobes did not believe the converts ready as yet to be entrusted with this responsibility.

The din without, the stir within, mingled dimly in Anastasia's ears. Christian that she was, she felt at this moment the impact between two different worlds, and it made her tremble. The light from a pine torch was burning low. The little girl stirred upon her braided mat; it rustled like the wind among drying cornstalks. She stood and waited; waited for Kahenta to move; but she did not. Still the woman waited, her eyes now fastened upon the boy, waited until all was over for both mother and child.

The little girl cried out in her delirium; but the small voice was smothered in the turmoil of the long house. One of the braves while preparing the chief for burial had staggered into a corner and lay face downward, groaning. At the farther end of the cabin a squaw shivered within her shawl and died. Through dragging hours Anastasia kept watch beside the stricken child whose life seemed to hang by a spider web that would not break. At every moment she feared that Tekakwitha would die, yet was almost more afraid that she would live. What could life be for the merry little one now? She had been her mother's dancing shadow, the life and laughter of the long house. Kahenta had taught her, small as she was, the gentle ways that she herself had learned in the land of the French. With her mother, Tekakwitha had withdrawn into the darkest corner during the orgies of the Dream Feast and when her father danced the war dance with the braves around the boiling kettle. Her brother would clap his hands as he watched; but she would turn her face away, cling to her mother, and hide with her behind the wide black shawl. If the child lived she would be adopted by her uncle Iowerano, who had been appointed according to the matriarchal custom of the Mohawks, then duly elected chief, in her father's place. She would be brought up by Karitha his wife, and Arosen his sister. How different they were from Kahenta! Would the latter's early influence be strong enough to shield the child from the pagan atmosphere which would inevitably surround her?

In the Mohawk village drunkenness and loose living were the custom. Girls were brought up in vanity. Women, even children participated in the torturing of enemies and fed upon their roasted flesh. There were some exceptions of course; but would Tekakwitha be one of these, without her Christian mother? Anastasia was filled with foreboding. She could envision the girl's future only as one of moral ruin or ceaseless struggle.

For ten days Tekakwitha swung between life and death.

Anastasia never left her, and her aunts were glad to be free from the care of her. Even when it was certain that Tekakwitha would live, her recovery was slow; so terrible were the ravages of the disease. Listlessly she lay in Anastasia's lap. Two weeks passed with but little improvement.

"Little bright-eyed squirrel, my pretty red-winged bird, soon you will run and play again, and fly with your swift little feet." The woman's voice was like a caress. But the child's eyes no longer danced, and Anastasia noticed that she turned them away even from the little light that came from the hole in the roof, which was the chimney and window combined.

"I cannot see you plain," the child cried out in fright.

"The smoke in the long house is heavy today." The woman's soothing voice replied but she shuddered in her heart. The disease was leaving its shadow for life. The large, liquid eyes had but half their former vision and the cheeks that had been round and dimpled were dented with disfiguring marks.

A weary month passed for Tekakwitha. Anastasia had to teach her anew how to walk. Feebly and gropingly she was finding her way once more about the long house. Iowerano, her uncle and now the new chief, with his wife and his sister was living in her father's lodge, so Tekakwitha did not have to leave the only home that she knew. Despite her disadvantages her uncle welcomed her as his adopted daughter. He had no children of his own; and what was more she was a girl, and that meant much to a Mohawk. She would learn the many useful arts of the squaw and in time she would bring a fine young brave into the household. Among the Iroquois a man upon marriage would come to live in the home of the bride. To her family it would therefore be a great enrichment to acquire another hunter to provide the game and the precious furs.

Mohawk women love their children, and the squaws of the long house were tender toward the bereft Tekakwitha. When her aunts Karitha and Arosen petted her, she responded with her ready smile; but she clung to Anastasia and to the corn-husk doll that her mother had made. Anastasia's heart was heavy when she had to leave the girl entirely to the care of her aunts. Reluctantly she dropped the bearskin curtain that seemed to shut Kahenta's child into a darkened world. "Poor little red-winged bird" she muttered to herself as she slowly turned away, into the direction of her own cabin.

CHAPTER

4 Tekakwitha looked with wonderment at the pale faces of the three visitors to whom her uncle was speaking. She marveled at their broad pantaloons and was fascinated by the silver buckles on their shoes; but how could men come through the forest or cross rivers carrying such strange large bowls upside down on their heads? Never had she suspected that people different from Indians were in the world. But they were kind people, these Dutch. They smiled and nodded and she heard her uncle welcoming them as dearest friends. Timidly she had withdrawn into a corner; but all three of them came to her and brought her beautiful things, handfuls of colored glass beads and shiny little shells. One of them even gave her a silver coin, something she had never seen before.

The year 1660 was half over, the virulence of the epidemic had abated and the Mohawks as they often did, were planning to move their village. Iowerano had always traded with the Dutch on friendliest terms and now, shrewdly enough, he wanted to solicit their aid in building the new castle, or village, of the Turtles on a neighboring hill. He had therefore invited them to come for a visit and talk things over.

"We have asked your help, my brothers," the chief began. "We must build a palisade for our new village at Gandawagué over the rapids. It is high up. Come, I will show you."

In front of the long house the view leaped over the edge of the plateau where Ossernenon lay near Schoharie Creek, down over the grain fields along the bank of the Mohawk, to a high point some miles to the North, in an angle between Auries Creek and the Mohawk.

"It is high up," the Dutchmen commented.

"Yes," said the chief. "Therefore we shall need horses from you." The leader of the Dutchmen lifted an eyebrow and looked at his companions. The chief continued undisturbed: "The Iroquois do not know horses, so we ask our brothers the Dutch to drive them for us and to drag the logs up the hill for a palisade."

The Dutchmen exchanged glances and grew restless. "Do you not see that we are tired?" they exclaimed. "We have traveled far through the forest. Our men are few and weary."

"But," said the chief straightening himself to the full height of his six feet, "the Iroquois are not used to such work. It is much more becoming to a settler than to a Mohawk warrior."

"Besides, you have no roads," the Dutch interposed. "Our horses could never get up there. You must excuse us, our friends, and manage to do it without us. See, as a token of friendship we have brought you fifty new hatchets."

"But come," the chief said in his grandest manner, "let us meet in the council long house and smoke the calumet."

The Dutch were friendly, even conciliatory; but they seemed suddenly pressed for time. They delivered their gifts and hurried back to the Hudson.

The chief handled one of the gleaming hatchets. A fierce light shot into his eyes. The red and blue paint in streaks over his prominent cheekbones, took on a more sinister aspect as he felt of the keen edge.

"These will cut the wood; they will also work well upon the heads of Frenchmen." He smiled to himself. "Really, the Mohawks are very cunning devils."

Tekakwitha heard it and shuddered.

As the year 1660 wore on and the last traces of the plague had disappeared, before the final evacuation of Osser-nenon the Indians gave themselves over to violent celebration. The Mohawks had great faith in the potency of the elk hoof as a good-luck charm. When the hunters caught an elk they would save the hoofs, scrape them, bore a hole, and string them together to be worn on special occasions. Night after night therefore, during these last days in the old village, the braves wore these talismans around their knees, rattling them frantically when, led by the sorcerers, they danced about the roaring fires lit to the demon Aireskoi. They made no offerings to Tharonyawagon, the national god and good genius. It was the evil one whom they had to propitiate.

"Forgive us, Aireskoi," they shrieked, "forgive us for not eating our enemies!"

Drunken braves reeled through the streets or lay about the square, and hungry dogs gnawed the remnant bones of many a feast.

Thus Ossernenon, though decimated by the recent plague, rocked with ribald song before its Indians folded their furs and skins, gathered their war implements and household utensils and moved in straggling procession down to the river and to Gandawagué their new village over the rapids. They went without the shadow of a premonition that other genera-tions would make their village live again, that a multitude would come to pray. On that deserted upland the martyred Jogues had met his torturers, and death. There too, René

Goupil his companion, had been killed for tracing the cross on the forehead of a Mohawk child, and ten years later, on that doubly consecrated spot Kateri Tekakwitha had been born. Heavily the burdened squaws climbed the steep slope along the west bank of Auries Creek, while silence descended like a presence upon deserted Ossernenon, a presence reminiscent of the severed head of Ondessonk placed long ago upon a palisade facing toward the North, a presence, guarding the unknown spot where René Goupil's body lies sheltered in his ravine.

CHAPTER 5

In the gardens of Beverwyck, now the city of Albany, the tulips were in full bloom. Polished windows gleamed in the spring sunshine and at the trading post beyond the palisade signs of life were visible. Canoes had been sighted on the Hudson. The Indians coming from the Mohawk Valley on their first visit for the year 1663, were bringing the fruits of their winter hunt.

"Pieter, Pieter" called a voice from the upper half of a Dutch door on Joncaer Street, out of which a moment later, a starched cap protruded.

"Let him run, Aleida," a man's voice interposed from within. "All the children of the town will be down at the northern gate. The Indians have come and will be unpacking their furs. Let him go!"

It was just as well; for small Pieter Van Clief paid no heed. His mother came out onto the stoop. Her round face and smiling blue eyes belied the little frown that had gathered above her straight nose. The duffle pants, blown to balloons by the fresh spring wind, were disappearing around a corner. The woman rattled the keys and scissors hanging from her belt, flecked some imagined dust from her broad petticoat, and turned back into the house.

All afternoon of the preceding day the young men of the settlement had taken turns carrying firewood to the trading house outside the palisade. The Dutch traders were at their post even before the canoes came into sight; but the Indians had just arrived and were busy undoing their packs. Within the stockade, looking through the apertures the children of the town formed a succession of round, curious eyes that were fastened on the faces of the Mohawks. One brave had a blue nose, and cheeks streaked with black. Another had red paint smeared like bloody cuts across his forehead. Still another had his face tattooed with animal images, a bear, an elk, a serpent. The children were frightened at the faces; but laughed at the strange Mohawk hairdress which varied from bristles running like a coxcomb down the center of a shaved head, to a shock of hair on only one side, or grotesque locks scattered about with shaved patches in between. The boys, especially, looked with admiration at the physiques of the braves; for the Mohawks were well built and many of them six feet tall.

The curiosity of the Indians vied with that of the children. They looked with interest through the open gate of the stout stockade at the strange Dutch doors and the wooden seats on the stoops. Every house had a garden and was overshadowed by a large tree under which the settlers milked their cows in the summertime. The red men marveled anew at the tiles, the woodwork, the ornamental iron that marked the home of Dominie Schaats, who had built the first brick house in the new world. Some of the older ones pointed out the house where Megapolensis had lived, the dominie who had hidden Ondessonk from the Mohawks.

In the trading house, business was in full swing.

"Brother," said Chief Iowerano to trader Van Loon, "I have come to trade with you; but I forewarn you to be more moderate in your demands than formerly!"

"Why, Brother?" the trader asked in surprise. "Are not my goods of equal value with those you had last year?"

"Perhaps they are," the chief replied, glad of an opportunity to repeat his grievances, "but mine are more costly because more scarce. The Great Spirit who has withheld from the white man the strength and ability to provide food and clothing for himself, has given him cunning and art to make guns and provide firewater, and by speaking smooth words to simple men when they have swallowed madness, they have little by little purchased their hunting grounds and made them into cornlands. Thus the beavers grow more scarce and the deer run farther back."

Iowerano was interested in the knives and hatchets, the silver bracelets and earrings; but when the trader offered him beads his lip curled.

"Your beads," he said brushing them aside, "are of no value. No warrior who has slain a wolf would wear them."

The trader toyed with his ruffles and smiled understandingly.

"But here are many things that you will like," he continued undeterred. "Here is a looking glass and here is a brass kettle in which your woman may boil her maize, her beans, and above all her maple sugar."

The chief shook his head. His skins were running low; but he picked up the mirror once more and looked at his reflection spellbound.

"For this I will give you a marten."

"Agreed!" said the trader, smiling and adjusting his sugar-loaf hat.

"This will be for Tekakwitha when her hair grows longer," the chief was telling himself.

But for the Indians, even when the trading was done,

the day was not complete without a celebration, a little taste
of the firewater that made a man glad. It was not long before
frenzied laughter, howls, and war whoops filled the air.
Within the stockade Dutch caps appeared at the windows and
soon the women in their colored petticoats were running out
into the street and hurrying to the north gate to collect their
children. Small Pieter Van Clief, now that the real fun was
beginning, would not move; but Aleida boxed his ears and
dragged him stumbling home. The sentries at the wooden
fort were on the alert; but the turmoil quieted, the Indians
dropped into a heavy sleep and lay scattered about the trading
house. Before the town was astir they had gathered together
their purchases. The depression after heavy drinking was
upon them. The firewater was gone and the last of their
furs had gone with it.

In sullen silence they retraced their way westward from
the Hudson, up the Mohawk Valley to the west side of
Auries Creek. The quiet beauty of the landscape was lost
upon them as they climbed the steep bank of the stream to
the Turtle castle. The light of maize fields against the darkness of the forest, the soft rolling of the hills with the river
curving between them, brought no home-coming joy. Gandawagué lay on an upper terrace that looked down upon the
plateau where old Ossernenon had been. Since so many had
died in the epidemic it was a smaller village, or castle, as the
Dutch called it. Nevertheless it was the fortified home of
the Turtle clan, and as such, the first from the East, of the
three Mohawk castles, with Andagoron, castle of the Bears,
as the second, and Tionnontoguen, castle of the Wolves and
the capital, as the third.

In addition Gandawagué remained the eastern gate to the
homeland of the Iroquois, this first American republic includ-

ing the five Iroquois nations. Of these the Mohawks were the fiercest. The Oneidas lived to the left of them; then the Onondagas, who were at the center of the Federation, who led in council, and whose chief lit the central council fire, surrounded by the fifty oyanders or sachems, who constituted the Iroquois senate. The Cayugas lived beyond the Onondagas and the Senecas who bordered upon Niagara, guarded the western gate. In its general aspect the Gandawagué of Auries Creek looked much like the other Iroquois villages, with its irregular cluster of bark long houses behind a wall of palisades and its central square with a scaffolding for the torture of captives.

Historians have not yet established with certainty the exact year of the removal of the Turtle village from Ossernenon to Gandawagué. Dutch records of the period assert that the Turtles were building a new palisade in the latter part of 1659. Apparently the epidemic of smallpox, the probable cause of the removal, was still raging during a part of 1660. Although the Indians could build their simple villages quickly, it is more than likely that such a transfer was not completed all at one time. Be that as it may, Tekakwitha, after the death of her parents spent six uneventful years in the first Gandawagué, on the south shore of the Mohawk and the west bank of Auries Creek.

Shortly after the return of the braves from their visit to the Dutch, Tekakwitha and her aunts were sitting about the fire. All morning she had been out gathering fagots and carrying water. Not content with supplying their own wants, the little girl brought water for everyone in the lodge who needed it. The fire was burning brightly. Although it made her eyes smart, she moved closer to it, borrowing a little of its fitful light for the beads that she was stringing into a necklace.

The child was small for her seven years, and delicately built. She had remained frail and half blind ever since her illness; but her quick intelligence, her amiable disposition, and the nimble fingers that promised unusual skill in the arts of Indian women, compensated for her physical handicaps. She was already plaiting corn leaves into shoes and stockings, beading her uncle's moccasins in designs of her own invention, and making curious little bowls out of bark.

"Lift your head, Tekakwitha," Karitha commanded. "I want to comb your hair."

Tekakwitha smiled and complied; but continued her work, bringing it up within her range of vision.

"At least she is not lazy," Arosen remarked. "The other children think of nothing but play and looking pretty, and their mothers comb and dress their hair for hours, especially when they go to the dance."

"But, Auntie," Tekakwitha said, "I couldn't go to the dances anyway because I'm so slow and must feel my way. And I can't play like other children. I could never catch the pebbles that they throw high up into the air. I can't even play hide and seek. If I run I stumble and fall, and I could never find anyone."

She laughed gaily, not in the least sorry for herself. It was much more fun to sit in a quiet corner and trace in beading some of the lovely pictures that came into her head. To go to the woods and finger the growing things, the cool leaves, the slippery pine needles, and to surprise the squirrels when they came from their hiding places was much more pleasant than running back and forth at hide and seek.

"Perhaps you can't find anyone," her aunt resumed; "but you surely know how to hide."

Tekakwitha laughed; for she knew that this was true.

Karitha had woven beads into the girl's shiny black hair, now long enough to braid, and was surveying her work with satisfaction. With an air of mystery she took something bright from under a rabbit skin where she had kept it hidden ever since the chief's return from Fort Orange, two weeks ago. It flashed in her hand and she held it up close, looked at it as though fascinated, and smiled and smiled at what she saw. Arosen, consumed with curiosity, leaned over her shoulder. She too smiled, laughed aloud, and shook her head in approval. Tekakwitha bending over her work paid no heed.

"Look, little owl — now you can see how pretty it is, the way I have dressed your hair," said Karitha holding the mirror up to her. Tekakwitha lifted her eyes. She did not look at her hair. For the first time she saw her face and all the tiny pits that the smallpox had dug into it.

CHAPTER 6

Many things happened in and about the Mohawk Valley in the year 1664. In 1663 consternation had shaken both Indians and Dutch at the massacre by the Mohicans of the whites at Esopus or Kingston. The Dutch renewed their treaty with the Mohawks, Fort Orange went into a state of defense, and three pieces of artillery loaned by the patroon, Van Rensselaer, were placed on top of the church. The settlers were gathered for safety into the fort known as Cralo, on the Van Rensselaer farm at Greenbush, while the sentries kept watch night and day.

In 1664 however, something totally different took place in the Dutch colony. While England and Holland were still nominally at peace, Charles II of England gave his brother, the Duke of York, a patent making him proprietor of a new English province which corresponded roughly with New Netherland. In the same year while the Dutch were still in possession, the English landed a force too strong for the Dutch governor, Stuyvesant, to resist. He therefore accepted the terms, and without any apparent rupture of peace New Netherland became New York and Beverwyck on the Hudson was called Albany. The treaty of Breda in 1667 confirmed this conquest.

To the Indians this change made little difference and the trading continued as always. The white man, however, was pushing his way farther and farther into the Mohawk Valley. Also in 1664, the large tract behind Fort Orange, sold in 1661 to the Sieur Van Corlaer by three Mohawk chiefs, was divided. The result was a settlement on the south bank of the Mohawk, which the Indians called Schonowe and the Dutch and English, Schenectady.

The Mohawks of Gandawagué were especially interested in the founding of this town which brought the white man almost to their door. Its wooden palaces and most of all the newly constructed sawmill aroused a wonderment amounting almost to awe. The Turtle chief, Iowerano, often visited his friend Van Corlaer, the most influential man of the town, who had always been on good terms with the Mohawks. As early as 1642 he had come to their village to secure the ransom of Father Jogues or Ondessonk, for whom he had shown great sympathy.

Meanwhile, in the long house of the chief an ancient Indian custom was repeating itself. Tekakwitha, aged eight, was betrothed to a boy but little older. This was frequently done with Indian children even in the cradle, and usually signified a seal of friendship between two families rather than a permanent bond. Tekakwitha was indifferent to the whole procedure and the boy was equally unconcerned, so nothing came of it. It was however a beginning, and both uncle and aunts constantly reverted to the subject of an early marriage for Tekakwitha. Iowerano had adopted another daughter, Ennita, an older girl; but it was upon his brother's child that his hopes were built. She, the daughter of a chief, must bring an outstanding warrior, a powerful hunter, into the cabin. Stern and dictatorial, he expected the docile Tekakwitha to bow to his slightest wish.

Young as she was, the aunts were already taking advantage

"What on earth are you doing, making that noise?" Arosen asked crossly. "Can't you hurry and give us something to eat?"

The girl was moving about quickly, preparing the sagamite. Uneasily she looked at the paling embers that could never make a kettle boil. The women waited, complained, and waited; but the congealed mass stirred only into a bubble or two. While they nagged at one another, scolded about the absent braves, tasted the tepid sagamite, Tekakwitha took her snowshoes from between the sapling beams, put on her red shawl, and fastened the burden strap about her forehead. Noiselessly she slipped out in the cold and beat her way down the slope.

More snow was falling upon a white world and white hills narrowed about the valley. Gandawagué, the castle of the Turtles, stood locked like a fastness behind its palisade. Nothing stirred but the driving snow and a little girl in a red shawl groping her way through the storm.

Alone in the forest, Tekakwitha plunged her hand far down into the snow in search of fagots. The trees cracked with cold as at the impact of an ax. All traces of a path were covered and she often staggered over slippery, uneven places. The wind beat her down into the snow; but she rose quickly every time and laughed at herself. She was happy out here, alone in the storm, happier than in the stagnant air of the long house. The wind whistling shrilly about her ears was a more pleasant sound than the scolding voices of her aunts. Content with her inner world, she loved being alone. The thought of giving pleasure or help to others spurred her on, and little Mohawk that she was, she felt at home even in this uneven battle with the elements. She did not turn back until it seemed as though the life had gone out of her feet, and her fingers were too numb to move. The only sense of feeling left in her was the dull tugging of the fagots fastened together with the twisted rope of bark at the end of the burden strap which had grown heavy upon her back.

At home in the lodge the women were still grumbling. Two of the five fireplaces were dark. In the others the glow was dying down. The squaws like dim shadows moved restlessly about in search of stray bits of wood.

"Where is Tekakwitha?" Arosen suddenly exclaimed. No one had noticed that the corner where she had been sitting bent over her strand of wampum, was empty.

"Tekakwitha, Tekakwitha!" Karitha began to scream. Uneasily she hurried to the front of the lodge and peered out; but an onslaught of wind blew the snow into her face and she turned back quickly, her teeth chattering.

"What shall I say to Iowerano if the child is lost?" she moaned.

"Look!" one of the women called, "someone has lifted the curtain and dropped it again."

"It is the wind," Karitha replied, shivering; nevertheless she went to the door; and she found the child leaning against the bearskin curtain, her back piled with wood. Karitha, forgetting to scold, picked her up quickly and carried her to the hearth. The fagots tumbled out of the burden strap, Ennita quickly lit a fire with them, and Tekakwitha could see the dreary faces light up at the warmth. Karitha and Arosen were chafing her icy fingers back to life. The grateful women gathered about her, filled a bowl with sagamite and forced her to eat while they plied her with questions. Her eyes were merry as she answered them:

"The North Wind slapped me in the face, then bound me fast to a hickory tree after making me stumble against it."

During the same storm a staggering army on snowshoes

crossing Lake George was nearing the dividing of the trail at the site of the future Fort William Henry. For some time the French, goaded to exasperation by the repeated forays of the Iroquois of whom the Mohawks were always the most active, had resolved once and for all to put an end to the menace. They therefore planned a surprise invasion of the Mohawk Valley in the dead of winter; and under Governor de Courcelle three hundred veterans of the wars of Louis XIV with two hundred French habitants had left Quebec on January 9, 1666.

By the third day many of them, partially frozen or with legs badly cut by the ice, had to be carried. On January 25, which was bitterly severe, a great number were taken back to the settlements. At the French forts along the Richelieu River the dwindling troops were reinforced, and on January 30, five hundred men pushed southward over Lake Champlain on sledges drawn by mastiffs through snow sometimes four feet deep. Then without stopping they stumbled along the narrow valley to Lake George. They had to keep moving or freeze. And the Blackrobe, Father Raffeix their chaplain, kept pace with them, sharing every hardship, spending himself meanwhile to inject his own courage into their flagging spirits.

They had reached the point where they expected to meet the promised Algonquin guides. With growing desperation, whipped by the wind that cut across the frozen waters, they scanned shores and islands in search of them. Neither Algonquin friends nor Iroquois foes were in sight. De Courcelle summoned Father Raffeix and they stood together looking toward the south, then toward the west. The unsuspecting squaws and the old men shivering in Gandawagué thought that they had nothing but cold and hunger to fear.

De Courcelle's forehead knitted to a frown. "The Algonquins have disappointed us," he said bitterly. "No white man's army has ever traveled these trails."

"No," said Father Raffeix, "only the Indians, and here and there a missionary."

"If we take the one leading southwest," the Governor resumed, "according to what the Algonquins told us, we reach a ford below the mouth of the Sacondaga, then we can go along that river to where it meets the Mohawk right at the first castle near Schoharie Creek."

"If we hit the southeasterly trail," de Courcelle continued, "we come to a lake. At its north end a path goes directly west to the Mohawk castles."

"There is great danger of losing the way," Father Raffeix warned, "since there are several diverging paths along this trail. One of them goes south along the west bank of the Hudson. We must not make the mistake of marching into the settlements of the Dutch."

"That would be awkward," de Courcelle said, with a glance at his stumbling men. "But it is almost impossible to find any trail in this weather." De Courcelle shook his head dejectedly as he turned aside to speak to his men.

Limbs were stiffening in the cold. The same north wind that beat Tekakwitha against the hickory tree lashed the face of the Blackrobe as he dropped to his knees in the untracked snow. He was marching with an army; but his thoughts were of peace, not war. The Jesuit's vision was in his heart, the dream of a mission that was to be, and his spirit reached out over the frozen miles, longing for the place where Isaac Jogues had met his martyrdom. And with the snow falling about him, he prayed for a share in continuing the work of Ondessonk.

De Courcelle and his army reached Ballston Lake; but from there they took the wrong trail. On February 9 they encamped within two miles of Schenectady, a march of three days from the first of the Mohawk villages. They were unaware of their mistake, and when on the same evening they encountered a party of Mohawks, they felt certain of having reached their destination. The Mohawks, simulating a retreat, drew sixty of the best French fusiliers after them into an ambuscade where nearly two hundred Indians, hidden behind trees, fired upon them, killing eleven French. The Mohawks escaped with only three slain and six wounded, and carried the news, with the heads of four of the French, to Schenectady. Instead of surprising the Mohawks the French were surprised, not only at finding themselves in a settlement of Dutch, but at learning that the colony had been taken over by the English.

When the report reached Albany three men of the town were sent at once to ask Governor de Courcelle why he had invaded the dominions of His Majesty of Great Britain without acquainting the English authorities with his intentions. De Courcelle bit his lip as he explained that he had brought his army to destroy the Mohawks, the enemies of the French, and that he had not heard that this was English territory. His face was flushed as he returned to his men, deeply disturbed at the news. "The King of England," he said to Father Raffeix, "is grasping at all America." The Blackrobe did not reply.

The Indians had gone back to their villages. The exhausted French troops who had accomplished nothing other than the proving of their heroism, were refreshed with provisions, especially bread and peas, bought from the Dutch. With renewed energy they set out on the march again, presumably in the direction of the Mohawk castles; but faced about, and with all possible speed returned to Canada.

CHAPTER "Tekakwitha, bring me my pipe."

The girl jumped up to obey. When Iowerano settled himself to smoke, with a look of contentment stealing over his face, she sat down on her mat again, picked up her deerskin collar and porcupine quills, and continued her work.

"I am glad, my Father," she ventured, "that you have come home from the warpath."

Iowerano puffed reminiscently. "It was a good fight," he answered. "The winter showed his teeth; but he cannot frighten a Mohawk. Instead the Mohawks frighten their enemies. The Mohawks are clever. You do not know how clever, little Tekakwitha, or how fierce." She always felt more secure when her uncle was in the long house, and happier than when alone with her aunts. He was all that she had, to take her father's place. He was severe and she knew that he could be cruel; but hidden under his gruffness there was a spark of affection for her, and she felt it.

They were sitting quietly when a sudden hubbub of voices broke the winter silence of the street. A moment and the chief was on his feet. "There is news!" he exclaimed just as the bearskin curtain opened and some half-dozen braves stormed into the long house. They were the first arrivals from Schenectady bringing word of the encounter with the French. The chief smiled grimly at the glowing account; but his face darkened when they told him that their two French prisoners had warned them that this summer a larger and better equipped army would make another attempt upon the Mohawk country.

Tekakwitha's fingers flew. She had lived intimately with stories of battle. Ever since she could remember, and she was ten years old, the war whoop had been a familiar sound in her ears. Again and again the braves had danced the war dance around the steaming kettle and hurried off on the warpath. She knew that they had crossed the border into Canada and harassed the French; but no white man's army had ever taken vengeance on the castle of the Turtles. What would happen if it did? Often during her short life her people had gone to war; but war had never come to them.

The braves had gone. Iowerano sat down again and blew rings of smoke into the air. "Let them come," he muttered, "let them come!"

But Tekakwitha did not forget the threat of the French. In the late days of spring whenever she walked to the well she scanned the horizon as far as her bedimmed vision would permit. Nothing appeared against the clear blue of the sky but the billowing hills, the dancing river, the dark green of the forest.

"They will not come." Iowerano laughed with his braves. "An empty boast! They wanted to frighten us; but they fear the Mohawk devils."

The other nations of the Iroquois, however, were more disquieted than the Mohawks by this new movement on the part of the French. Therefore in the summer following de Courcelle's expedition ten ambassadors from the Iroquois League met in Quebec and signed a treaty of peace. The

Indians, among whom the Mohawks were not adequately represented, asked that the Blackrobes be sent to them. They promised to accept their teaching, offered to trade with the French via Lake George, and assured them of a welcome in their long houses.

The deputies were scarcely two or three days on their journey home from Quebec when news came that the Mohawks had surprised a party of Frenchmen from Fort St. Anne, who had gone on the hunt. In the attack they had murdered a captain of the French army. Evidently the Mohawks were far from thoughts of peace. For a time they remained unpunished; but the French had not finished with them. Quietly, after the summer heat had cooled, three hundred light bateaux and bark canoes slipped from Fort St. Anne into Lake Champlain and skimmed toward Lake George, carrying two cannon, six hundred soldiers with as many habitants, and one hundred Hurons and Algonquins under de Tracy, lieutenant general of the French armies in the New World.

CHAPTER 9

It was early October of the year 1666, and in the Mohawk villages the merriment of harvest time was about to begin. This year there would be great celebration. The three sister goddesses, the Corn, the Bean, and the Squash had been generous. But this did not detain Ratorats, the indefatigable hunter. He felt the call of the forest and went far in pursuit of the fox. He had chased it up toward the mountaintops and when he reached a towering summit he stood for a moment while his quick eye swept the glowing landscape and the two lakes far below. In a flash he saw, understood, and bounded back through the woods until he reached Gandawagué with the cry of alarm panting in his throat.

The warriors heard, ran for their muskets and hatchets, their bows and arrows. The women in the maize field heard, dropped the ears of corn, and stumbled up the hill to the village. Tekakwitha coming from the spring heard, and with eyes blinded by the sun groped her way back to the long house. Another runner sped westward over the two leagues to Andagoron, the village of the Bears; on to the castle of the Wolves and the strongest fort of the Mohawks.

It did not take the people of Gandawagué long to gather provisions and the most valuable of their belongings, and to move at once to the castle of the Bears. Tekakwitha fled with them, the most silent of all that silent company. Hurriedly she had fastened her burden strap and crowded into it all the supplies that her slender shoulders could support. Underneath, where no one could see it, she had hidden her dearest treasure, the corn-husk doll that her mother, Kahenta, had made for her.

After a hasty consultation at Andagoron, the castle of the Bears, all fled together to Tionnontoguen, the castle of the Wolves. It lay hidden behind a sharp turn in the valley that shuts off the opening between the mountain known as the Nose and a similar summit on the south side of the river. It was this setting that gave the Mohawk capital its name of Tionnontoguen, which means the approach of two mountains. Within its triple palisade the Indians crowded the women and children and stored their provisions for the winter. Tekakwitha trembled beside her aunts while they waited. There was no time to summon the Oneidas, their neighbors to the West; so this final stand against the French depended upon three or four hundred Mohawks alone.

The braves were in their best fighting trim, ready to stake all in defense of this their strongest fortress. They took up their position on the platform or scaffolding that extended between the three rows of posts or palisades, twenty feet high, that walled the town. As a protection for the warriors in this otherwise exposed position, the outermost wall rose a man's height above the two other palisades and was covered near the top with a surface of bark. In case the enemy should set fire to the base of the palisade, bark water tanks stood on the inner platform and a bark fence at some distance guarded the approach.

De Tracy meanwhile, undeterred by any thought of the English, had crossed the Hudson, reached Saratoga, passed

near Ballston, and curved onto the trail westward meeting
the Mohawk River at Amsterdam. From this point a short
march up the Mohawk Valley brought the French army,
guided by its Algonquin friends, directly to Gandawagué.
In the village nothing stirred as he approached. The gates
of the palisade stood open. No one was working in the fields
along the river bank. Andagoron, too, was empty. De Tracy
captured the deserted villages and hamlets one after another,
and with his two cannon and twelve hundred men armed as
for warfare among European nations, hurried on to
Tionnontoguen.

Through the tense hours the Mohawk warriors peered
down into the valley. But the twin mountains closed the view.
They would not be able to see the French until they were
almost upon them. They had sent no scouts to reconnoiter.
Every man was needed, and the French in rapid approach had
left no room for doubt or even conjecture. Smoke in the
distance told the Indians that their fields and cabins lay in
ruins; and a fierce and desperate yell shook the waiting village. They must propitiate Aireskoi the war god. As a last
minute resource, working against time, a few surviving captives were dragged to the square to be tortured and burned
with solemn rites.

In her own village Tekakwitha was never present at such
a scene. Perhaps the cruel spirit shown by other women of
her tribe had been left out of her fashioning, perhaps the
suffering of her own frail and overtaxed body gave her a
fellow feeling for those in pain. Not only was there no urge
toward cruelty in her, but she could not bear even to see
anyone hurt. At the familiar orgies of torture to which every
Mohawk child quickly became accustomed, she would invar-
iably run away, either into a corner of the cabin or to hide

herself in the woods. "It is Kahenta in her," the aunts would say. "What kind of a Mohawk are you?" others taunted.

Nearer came the French, while the cries of the burning victims filled the air and Tekakwitha, quivering from head to foot, hid her face in the folds of her shawl. She could not run away, huddled as she was between the other women and children. When she fled up the valley with her people a sense of wrong burned within her at the cruel uprooting, the first impact from a strange outside world that could drive the Indians from their homes, destroy their villages, then come to kill them. And here at Tiennontoguen she sensed the desperation of the braves, saw the haunted look in the eyes of the squaws, and felt their anguish. But now, horrified at what her people were doing in the very face of their own danger, she almost wished that the French would come and draw all the braves to the palisades and that she might carry water to help keep the bark tanks filled.

And the French did come. Between the two mountains they filed into view. The demoniac rites in the square were barely over when the women and children were hurried out of the village to the higher hills beyond the fortifications, and hidden in the woods. Tekakwitha stumbled after her aunts. Dimly she saw the tall figure of her uncle high upon the platform with his musket pointed toward the valley. Then the wine-red trees closed around her and the stillness of the forest descended upon the stricken group waiting in silence as Indians do.

As soon as the French army came within reach, arrows flashed and bullets whistled sharply downward from the palisade; but no disturbance was evident in the well-ordered ranks now forming into position. Deliberately the two cannon were brought into position, and de Tracy prepared the attack in regular form. The Mohawks knew that their hour had come and saw the utter hopelessness of resistance. Without awaiting the opening fire, with all the agility of which they were masters they deserted the palisades and fled, leaving behind a few old men too helpless to move, and the dying and dead victims of the demon's sacrifice.

The French climbed up to the plateau and into the silent village. Again the Blackrobe, Father Raffeix, had marched with the troops. This time he had reached the destination of his desire, the land of the Mohawks. In the square, over the ashes of the recent fires he planted a cross. As he looked over the landscape, down the steep terraces to the river at the North, the ravine with its ferns and late berries at the West, and beyond to the woods touched with the poignancy of autumn, his heart prayed for the hidden Indians as he intoned the *Te Deum*.

Twelve hundred voices broke into song and for the first time since the creation of the world, the Mohawk Valley throbbed with the music of praise. The waiting women heard. Tekakwitha, listening for the turmoil of battle, then wondering at the silence, was stunned by this strange and sudden singing that seemed to shake the hills and set the trees to quivering. Her face lit with the thrill of a new beauty, something overpoweringly human added to the only loveliness that she knew, that of the forest, the waving grain, and the hills through which the curving river ran. This was different from the human voices to which she had been accustomed, different from the shrieks of the tortured, the hollow singing of captives, the war whoop of the Mohawks. This was not like their harvest songs, not like their chanting over the dead.

After their flight from the wall the braves, sullen with defeat, gathered in the forest near their families and waited;

waited until the last of the French had disappeared behind the Nose and its neighboring mountains, leaving Tionnonto-guen hemmed by a wall of blazing palisades. Then the low wail of the squaws rose from among the trees and stealthily the silent warriors came out of hiding. Not one of them had received the slightest wound; but their Mohawk world was destroyed.

De Tracy lost no time speeding back through the valley. On October 17 he paused, not far from Gandawagué, planted a cross, affixed the arms of Louis XIV to a post, and took solemn possession in the name of the King of France. He had not massacred one Indian, nor did he take a single captive with him as he led his army, intact, back to Canada. Father de Raffeix looked upon the blackened fields, the ruined villages as he passed. He had been powerless to prevent this destruction which the French regarded as a necessary punishment for the Mohawks. He had done what he could. At Tionnontoguen, their capital, he had offered a Mass and was leaving a benediction upon the desolate land. "Poor children!" he whispered under his breath. "The Blackrobes will make it up to you."

In disordered bands the braves, followed by a few dogs, squaws, some of them with papooses upon their backs, and children, straggled back down the valley to seek what was left of their homes. Anastasia Tegonhatsihongo had found Tekakwitha and held her tightly by the hand as they followed the speechless chief and the two women to Auries Creek. Against a background of crumbling cabins the newly erected cross stood straight. Anastasia knew it when she saw it, the long absent sign of the Blackrobes who, years ago, had vanished from the valley. Tekakwitha saw it and wondered at the strange apparition.

Life began again, this time in all its drabness. Tekakwitha with her customary energy helped to prepare the bark for the repairing of her uncle's long house, a rugged apprenticeship for a child of ten. The fires were lit; but there was scarcely food to cook as the days chilled into winter. The game her uncle caught was scant. The fields had burned to barrenness. Ears of corn did not, as usual, hang from the lodge poles. There were no beans, there was no squash. They lived on roots and the berries that they could find. Tekakwitha often returned with her basket empty; but tirelessly, wrapped in her red shawl, she gathered wood for the fire and dug for the unpalatable roots. It was harder now to battle against the wind. In hunger and cold the people of the devastated village shivered through the winter.

Spring came at last and with it great changes and a general stir among the Mohawks. They were looking for new sites on which to rebuild their castles. Tekakwitha often crossed the river now and helped her people clear the cornfields on the northern side. "Next year," Iowerano predicted, "after the bark will peel, we shall build a new village again."

The humiliated Mohawks, who for years had stubbornly opposed the treaties between the four other Iroquois nations and the French, were eager now for a permanent peace, and sent their deputies to Quebec. The Mohicans from New England and along the Hudson, taking advantage of the defeat of the Mohawks, made repeated raids upon the latter's hunting grounds. As a result the Mohawks, grown uneasy, were anxiously awaiting the return of their emissaries from Quebec.

In 1667 a new life dawned upon the stricken valley. All five nations of the Iroquois were at one with the French. Kahenta's long past, homesick prayer for peace was answered at last.

CHAPTER 10

It was late July and the sun lay like a path of fire over the Mohawk River. A small fleet of canoes approaching the southern shore was nearing the end of a long journey. Among the Indian deputies returning from Quebec sat three Frenchmen in long black robes. They were looking up to the top of the hill at all that was left of Gandawagué since de Tracy's destructive campaign.

"The blood of Jogues!" Father Frémin whispered almost under his breath. Father Bruyas heard. It was his own thought made articulate. Father Pierron, youngest of the three and the most recently arrived from France, was silent; but a new light burned in his eyes.

Tionnontoguen, the castle of the Wolves, and the Mohawk capital, was celebrating the return of better days with a tumult of debauches and was in no condition to receive the emissaries of Onnontio, as they called the French governor of Canada. It was necessary, therefore, that they be detained for a few days at Gandawagué as guests in the cabin of Iowerano. Sachems and war chiefs had come down to the river to lead them with all formality up the ascent to the town where ceremonies of welcome awaited them.

The people had gathered in the square where more than twenty years ago some from among them had received Father Jogues with iron rods and abusive words while they forced him to run the torturing gauntlet. Now the Blackrobes came again, with presents in their hands and a blessing upon their lips. Iowerano gritted his teeth; but he knew his duty as chief. To receive the missionaries and permit them to live among the Iroquois was one of the conditions of peace that the French imposed. Behind these humble, unarmed men stood the power of the King of France. With the eloquence that is the gift of the Iroquois, Iowerano made his speech of welcome.

"Stay with us, O Blackrobes," he urged. "Sleep in our cabins and let our women feed you with their cooking. Bring to us the wisdom of the Frenchman. Teach us of Rawenniio, the lord and master of your world."

Tekakwitha stood in bewilderment on the outskirts of the crowd. Was this her uncle speaking? Never had she heard him mention the name Rawenniio. Who was this lord and master of the white man's world?

Meantime Iowerano had seated himself within the birch-bough circle of council and was solemnly passing the pipe of peace. In silence Blackrobes and Indians smoked the calumet together. Then Father Bruyas, superior of the missionaries, rose.

"Mighty chief of the Mohawks," he began, "we have come, not to teach you the wisdom of the French or that of any mortal; but the wisdom of the Holy Spirit and of Life Eternal."

He drew the crucifix from his girdle, held it high, and told them of the Redeemer who had suffered and died to save the Indian as well as the white man and to lead them both to heaven.

"I pray to Rawenniio," he concluded, "that this peace of welcome may be a sign of the peace of God, the peace that the world cannot give."

Again there was silence while the peace pipe circled around the council group. Then Iowerano rose and with solemn strides carried the calumet to the center of the birch-bough enclosure and stood beside the council fire. Toward the east he blew the smoke, then to the west, to the north, and finally toward the sky, saying:

"To the world and to its Master the smoke of the Mohawk rises."

Tekakwitha listened closely and her eyes followed every movement. She had seen the cross in the hands of the Blackrobe and her bedimmed eyes strained toward the figure upon it. Suffering! Salvation for the Indian! Did suffering and salvation belong together? She recalled the Blackrobe's words and her mind groped among them. Suffering she understood. She knew it in her body and had known it in her heart ever since she could remember. With this awareness, her memory also began to grope, grope as her hands were so accustomed to do, and she found again the fevered darkness from which as a child she had awakened with an emptiness and a terror inside of her. Both grew vivid in the remembering; but this had been their beginning. Behind them was joy and the memory of a face, a face with love in it! And she knew that it was her mother.

The council fire died down, the people withdrew to their cabins, and the Blackrobes came to the long house of the chief. Tekakwitha was waiting to lift the curtain, to show them to their mats, to present the bowl of sagamite in welcome. Earlier in the day her uncle had grunted his commands. She was to be at the service of the Blackrobes throughout their stay.

The air was stifling and the odors that assailed the nostrils of the missionaries aroused no appetite for the contents of the kettle steaming over the fire. Scraps of belated sunlight dropped mistily through the opening above the hearth, window and chimney combined, and the dense smoke made the eyes of the missionaries smart painfully. The Indians in customary fashion crowded into the long house and circled about, curious to have a closer view of the Blackrobes, who smiled affably despite their difficulties in swallowing the unpalatable food. And Tekakwitha, forgetting her shyness, smiled warmly in return as, mindful of her duty, she hovered over her guests, eager to render service.

"God bless you, my child," said Father Frémin in Iroquois as she handed him water fresh from the spring, in a bark bowl of her own making. No one had ever spoken such words to her. Who was this God whose name the visitors used so familiarly, and with a tone of affection? Was He the same as Tharonjawagon? He could not be Aireskoi the cruel one. She shuddered inwardly at the bare possibility. From all that she knew of the lore of her tribe, she loved Hiawatha best, the one whom her people still called the Great Peace. The Blackrobe had spoken also of peace, a peace that meant something different from not being at war with the French. But Hiawatha was a man, not God. Sometime when no one was there to listen, she would ask the Blackrobes.

In the darkness of that first night, with the braves snoring around them, the Jesuits lay side by side upon their mats. This was the mission in its reality, stripped of the glamour that comes at the first call and fires the soul. This was the destination that beckoned from afar, uprooted men from their homes, and drew them over perilous seas into the depths of forests. Silently, with myriads of gnats circling about them and an army of mosquitoes pricking their flesh, sickened by the stench of the cabin and the ill digested food, all three were praying, each in his individual way, the self-giving prayer of the Jesuit: "Suscipe!" It was the cry of Ignatius: "Take, O Lord!"

The spirits of the martyred ones were near them tonight. Their blood was in this soil. Before an uneasy sleep fell upon them, Fathers Bruyas and Frémin remembered Brébeuf and Jogues; but Father Pierron was thinking of Chabanel, whose enthusiasm had turned into revulsion, who failed to learn the language, whose stomach could not stand the stench, but who vowed to stay until he died.

Tekakwitha lifted the jug from her shoulder, sat down at the foot of an oak tree, and closed her burning eyes. Because of their weakness she seldom ventured out into the noonday sun; but the water had run low. Nor did she ever linger like this on her way from the well even when the jug weighed upon her. It was not heavy today. Quite the contrary. The thought of the three guests whom she was serving added lightness to her step.

Never before had someone thanked her for the slightest attention. Never before had anyone asked whether she was tired. All the child in her reached out mutely to the gentle Fathers who went to visit the sick of the village, gathered the children about them, and told all who would listen such new and beautiful things.

She had to sit down and think for a while, here in the forest where she was alone. A strange and sudden light had penetrated into the solitude of her personality. Instinctively she believed and trusted the Blackrobes and they had said that the white man's God was just as much the God of the red man, that He had a father's love not only for the French, but for the Mohawks, even for their Mohican enemies, for all the people of the world. The Blackrobes called Him Rawenniio, which means the true God. They said that He is everywhere; that everyone, even the smallest child, may speak to Him at any time and He will always hear. Tekakwitha thought it all over. Her clouded eyesight, her disfigurement together with her natural shyness and reserve, had tended to set her apart from the teeming distractions of Mohawk life.

She was able therefore, intelligent as she was, to grasp an inner reality with the concentration of all her forces and with more sureness of purpose to keep it alive in that hidden world that had long been growing within her.

Tekakwitha smiled up into the trees. She was glad now, no matter what those about her had said, that she had always been repulsed by the torturing of enemies. If Rawenniio is the true God, one must do as He wishes. If He loves all people, no one must hate or torture anyone else. If He loves everyone, there was a place even for her, disfigured and unfit though she was, and the dreary life warmed from within.

A sound along the earth, falling upon her quick ear, roused her. Not far away, as though her thoughts had assumed a visible form, she saw the Blackrobes walking at their prayers. She had often observed that at regular intervals they withdrew in the direction of the forest and she marveled at their ordered lives amid the confusion of the long house. And yet they seemed to belong entirely to those around them. She hoped that they had not seen her. She too had wanted to be alone. Quickly lifting the jug back to her shoulder she climbed the slope up to the village.

Father Bruyas looked at the sun. "It is time to return to the cabin," he said, slipping his finger into his breviary.

"Some day perhaps," Father Pierron half whispered, "there will be a chapel, and the Angelus will echo through the valley."

"Look at little Tekakwitha," Father Frémin said pointing, "carrying that heavy jug. The child never rests."

"Who could have been her teacher?" Father Pierron exclaimed. "She has the manners of a well brought up French girl."

Father Frémin shook his head and smiled. "God plants His flowers in strange, wild places," he said.

Three days were over and the Blackrobes were spending their last evening in Gandawagué. While rings of smoke circled peacefully from the calumets a sudden shriek split the stillness and in the distance a dog howled. The screams gathered force. As at a signal, yells, war whoops, and the frantic barking of dogs shook the night into a tumult. Braves and squaws stumbled out of their cabins crying: "The Mohicans, the Mohicans!" as they ran toward the palisade. Their fears were confirmed. A band of prowling Mohicans had scalped a squaw just outside the gate to the village, and had disappeared into the forest.

Father Frémin outran the chief and was one of the first to reach the Mohawk woman. He dropped to his knees beside her and whispered hurried words of comfort into her ear. She tossed and moaned and would not listen. The time was short, the pain would soon be over, happiness for ever and ever was within her reach, he could promise it; but she spurned his pleading. He spoke more urgently, of God, of her soul that would never die, of heaven that is so beautiful. Four times she turned away, four times, with mounting fervor, he tried again. Eternal life and love and joy!

Tekakwitha, drawn with pity for the woman, had come

close. She stood spellbound as she witnessed the struggle of the priest for the soul of the dying squaw. Every time that the woman turned her bleeding head away Tekakwitha shuddered, fearing that it was the end. Would the Blackrobe grow tired or angry and let the poor creature die? No, he would not. She could see it in his face. He stooped lower. This time the woman did not turn away. Blindly her hands reached out toward the Blackrobe and Tekakwitha saw him take a small flagon from his pocket and pour water quickly over her head, in the form of a cross. The squaw grew quiet then, and in a few moments she was dead.

Tekakwitha scarcely breathed, and a powerful impulse seized her to run to the Blackrobe, to beg him to pour the water over her too; but she looked up, and in the excited crowd she saw her uncle's face. His lips were set and the cold hatred in his eye chilled her and kept her where she was.

CHAPTER 11 The shadow of the Mohicans gathered like a dark cloud and hung heavily over the land of the Iroquois. On both sides of the river there was movement. The Mohawks were fortifying the new castles on the northern shore. Evidently they had not altogether abandoned the old sites; or they may have added settlements for captives, since there were at this time perhaps as many as seven villages, which was an unusual number.

With her family Tekakwitha had migrated again; this time to the northern bank of the river near Cayadutta Creek, a few miles to the west of her former home, where the plateau of a sharply cut hill had become the village of Caughnawaga, so called from its position at the rapids of the river. With the squaws she had worked at the building of the new long house. As always, two rows of saplings had been planted, their tops bent and tied across the intervening space. Horizontal poles held the arched ribs in place and the whole was covered with square pieces of bark. The openings in the roof, serving both as windows and chimneys with overlapping pieces of bark to keep out the rain, left the new cabins dark as the old ones had been.

Once more the smoked meat and the dried corn hung from the ridgepoles of the roof. The wooden mortar and pestle for the pounding of corn, the bark bowls and utensils were in their places. Baskets of wampum beads to be strung into belts stood in corners, skins lay spread over the sleeping-shelves along the walls of the cabin, rush mats were strewn down the center where families gathered at mealtime, and the matrons had assigned a special lodge seat to every member of their respective households. Apparently life in the new village would continue in its customary way; but the squaws no longer worked unmolested in the cornfields on the margin of the river. Bands of Mohicans or other warring tribes now kept them in a constant fear of death. This serious frame of mind rendered them the more responsive to the new influence that had come into the valley. In every corner of it the Blackrobe was making his presence felt.

After their short visit at Gandawagué, the village of the Turtles, the three Jesuits had gone to Tionnontoguen where a public reception awaited them and where Father Frémin delivered an address in the name of the French governor. From the top of a pole hung an unusually long wampum belt. With it came the message from Onnontio that thus the first Iroquois would hang who dared to kill a Frenchman or any of his allies. The Mohawks made eloquent response. They delivered the captives demanded of them, offered the choice of a site for the erection of a chapel, and proposed to go to work at once.

As a result Father Frémin founded Saint Mary's Mission at Tionnontoguen, Father Bruyas went to the Oneidas, and Father Pierron was charged with the remaining Iroquois villages, among which he came and went with indefatigable energy. While Mohawks and Mohicans were burning and devouring each other with the Mohawks trying desperately to rid themselves of the fierce marauders, the Blackrobes were fighting an equally dramatic battle to expel Satan from the life of the valley. The people were possessed by their sorcerers and medicine men and were the slaves of dreams that drove them into a frenzy of excesses. It was at this period that Father Pierron wrote home to France that drunkenness and immorality were the divinities of the country.

The Mohawk chiefs themselves began to realize that the Blackrobe was right when he said that drink had a foreign demon more to be dreaded than those worshiped in their dreams. And it saddened the missionaries to remember that it was the white man who had first given the Indian firewater to drink. During the frequent periods of debauchery when for three or four days a village would run wild, Father Pierron thought with terror of a growing girl whose modesty and sweetness had so deeply impressed him and his companions during their stay in her uncle's cabin. Could she remain unsullied amid such filth? They could do but little for her in so short a time and under the disapproving eye of her uncle. The priest thought that he had seen her once or twice on the edge of the crowd, small and hidden among the shawls of the squaws. Perhaps it was on the day of his return from the journey to Quebec in October of 1668 or when he brought the pictures that he had painted for instructing the Indians in the truths of Faith.

But Tekakwitha gave no sign. On the occasions when Father Pierron passed through the village, and the people, especially the squaws, gathered about him, she was much too timid to approach. The fear of her uncle may have been an added reason for keeping her aloof. At any rate her lips remained sealed and no one saw the frequent longing in her eyes while she labored at her all too heavy household tasks or threaded her wampum beads into designs of beauty. She was growing in silence and from within.

It was at about this time that Tekakwitha's aunts decided that in accordance with the customs of the race, she should undergo the so-called Puberty Rites. This period was one of supreme importance and was believed to influence the person for the remainder of his or her life. It was in a sense a retreat, and charged with a certain mystical quality by reason of which a girl, for instance, would influence others by whatever she thought or did during this time. Therefore she was isolated either in a hut, a closed room, or behind a curtain where for four days or longer she was attended only by her mother or some older woman. She was believed to influence even the things around her. She ate sparingly, drank little or no water, and was absolutely forbidden the use of salt. Among the Iroquois she had even her own set of eating utensils. When she emerged from this seclusion she was no longer a girl, but a woman with all a woman's responsibilities.

For Tekakwitha, accustomed to solitude and loving lonely places, this was no ordeal. It was a relief to have this respite from the monotony of household duties and from the noise of voices, to dwell for a time securely within the depths of her own thoughts. For her who at so early an age had accepted responsibility and known the hurt of suffering, the step from girlhood to womanhood was scarcely perceptible.

She came out of her seclusion, went to the forest, and carved into a hidden tree the Blackrobe's symbol, the Sign of the Cross.

CHAPTER 12 It was the hour of darkness before dawn, August 18, 1669. Tekakwitha stirred uneasily in her sleep, then woke with a start to the sound of musket fire and wild cries. At least three hundred Mohicans from near the seacoast of Massachusetts were beating at the eastern door of the five nations. They had come with the deadly intent not to harass the Mohawks, but to crush them, and the famous Chackatabutt whose name means House Afire led the attack.

The discharge of musketry had roused the men, women, and children of the Turtle village into a bedlam of screams and war whoops. The braves grasped their guns and hatchets and rushed to the palisade. The squaws followed, armed with knives or any other weapon at hand, in case of a breach in the wall, and while the men warded off the attack the women were making bullets. Although the Mohicans, sometimes called Loups, made no progress against the fort, four Iroquois had at the very outset fallen dead from the platform, two more were wounded, one of them dying shortly afterward. Tekakwitha with the other young girls had come to help wherever needed and she soon found her place among the wounded and the dying. Meantime the nearest village had caught the alarm and made a sally upon the enemy. The flight and carnage in all directions caused the news to reach

Tionnontoguen that Caughnawaga, often still called Ganda-wagué, was besieged, that all the young men had fallen, and the whole country was lost.

The news spread rapidly to the other Mohawk villages. By eight o'clock of the same morning their warriors had arrayed themselves in their most valuable garments and without confusion and without a leader went in full force to meet the enemy. Father Pierron accompanied the first group; but upon arrival they heard only the lament of the women over the death of the bravest of their men. The Mohicans had retired after two hours of obstinate fighting, and the squaws were seeking their dead.

Medicine men and sorcerers were not in evidence. Father Pierron, somewhat of a doctor himself, had ridiculed their diabolic practices so effectually that they no longer performed in his presence; but he sickened as he saw that outside the walls a hideous human sacrifice to Aireskoi was in preparation. One Mohican warrior had been left behind. An Iroquois had already cut off his hands and feet, flayed him, and was stripping his flesh for eating. A wave of hopelessness swept over the priest until he looked at the bereft women and saw among them a small figure that he recognized. A young girl was on her knees beside a wounded Mohawk. The shawl had slipped from her head, and he saw the look upon her face.

After a few days of siege the Mohicans retreated toward the Dutch settlements. Just above Hoffman's Ferry some miles west of modern Schenectady, on the north side of the Mohawk River they entrenched themselves on a steep and rocky hill. At Caughnawaga, or Gandawagué as we shall continue to call the Turtle village, the women were preparing provisions for the warpath. That Iowerano's supply might be abundant Tekakwitha worked quickly, adding sometimes maple sugar, sometimes other seasoning to the pounded corn already twice charred or dried for purposes of war. With but little delay the armed warriors assembled, their deerskin pockets filled with crushed corn, ready to set out in pursuit of the Mohicans.

Tekakwitha, silent and tense with concern, followed her uncle as closely as she could down to the river where the canoes were lined against the bank, ready for departure. Even among the stalwart Iroquois one figure towered over the rest as with customary agility they leaped into their canoes and glided from the shore. It was the indomitable Kryn, surnamed the Great Mohawk, under whose leadership they were going into battle. The swift current carried them around the bend toward deserted Ossernenon and the settlements of the whites while the farewells of the women still trembled over the water. The squaws knew that a decisive struggle between two of the most warlike tribes of red men was at hand.

But the wounded needed care, the dead had to be prepared for burial. Often, during the heavy hours that followed, the women went to the spring and returned with but few words among them. Their hands were busy; but their hearts watched and waited, oppressed with the fear of what might come upon them. Tekakwitha, young as she was, felt the weight of this suspense.

It was dark in the long house when she returned, exhausted from much drawing and carrying of water. No one was there. Not a single fire was lit. The silence around her came close, almost touching the solitude within her. For once the two worlds, the outer and the inner, flowed into one another and mingled. For once the noise and the tumult seemed beyond the horizon of both. Rumors of a desperate battle twenty miles away hovered restlessly over the village. Her heart ached for her suffering people. In danger she was one of them. In periods of security she felt herself alien, though theirs was the only life that she knew.

What room was there for her in this teeming Mohawk world? The distaste that she felt for their dances and feasts, their wild celebrations, was something that was deeply in her and had grown with her. It was the same with the idea of marriage. Her aunts were constantly hinting at it and she knew that when the time would come, her uncle would exact unquestioning obedience to his commands. She shrank at the thought of marriage. Other girls even at her age were already looking forward to it. She could not. Besides, who would ever care for Tekakwitha? To whom could she, disfigured, half blind as she was, ever be a joy? And even if she could, having seen the life that was general among the Mohawks, her very spirit shrank from such companionship. Her own inner urge, her low opinion of herself, fostered, perhaps even conditioned by the physical disabilities that set her apart from others, engendered a timidity and a love of solitude that grew with the years. The very fact that she could not walk freely in the sun, the necessary shawl over her head, protecting her from too strong a light, contributed to the tendency toward retirement. Always, despite the relentless impact of life from without, she sought the quiet, hidden places and to be alone in them.

The sound of voices broke in upon her thoughts. Karitha and Arosen were returning and many women with them. Soon the cabin was filled with lamentations and futile questioning: "What of the battle? How many of their braves had fallen by this time? Would the Mohicans come again, destroy their village, and take them all captive?" Tekakwitha listening in silence trembled at the thought.

On the following day in the middle of the afternoon the news of victory came. The intrepid Chackatabutt was slain and some of the noblest of the Mohicans had fallen at his side. Those who escaped had fled. Father Pierron, who remained with the people of Gandawagué during the days of suspense, left for the battlefield at once and alone. The wounded and the dying had need of him. He must try also to temper the barbaric aftermath of victory, to make the Iroquois understand that they owed their deliverance to God. He arrived before nightfall and it is his report that tells the story of the battle of Kinaquariones.

Night had overtaken the Mohawks in their pursuit of the Mohicans and they sent spies in advance to track the enemy to his hiding place. "Koué Koué — who goes there?" a startled sentry called. No one answered so he did not give the alarm; but the Mohicans were so securely entrenched that the Iroquois could not make an attack. They prepared an ambush, therefore, in a craggy pass that commanded the route to the Dutch. On the following morning the Mohicans having broken up camp, walked in single file along the route and twelve of them were killed.

The Mohicans rallied where they had encamped. The Iroquois overtook them. Fiercely the Mohicans resisted; but the main body had to recede before the fury of the Iroquois. Ten of the Mohicans, however, made a last stand within the earthworks, ready to resist to the end. This was a terrible obstacle to the almost victorious Iroquois; but their courage held firm while they tried to dislodge the unyielding ten. Behind a fallen tree that they carried as a shield, one by one they advanced. A heavy fire from all sides killed many of the Iroquois until night put an end to the bloody fight. On the following morning they returned to the charge; but the Mohicans had fled, leaving the Iroquois masters of the field.

Two days after the battle, wild with triumph, the victors were marching homeward with their collection of scalps, marching to the tuneless singing of several bands of captives. Father Pierron saw that he could do nothing to prevent these barbaric demonstrations after such a victory, and he knew as well that upon arrival at the castle of the Turtles, in the white heat of hostility toward a foe once so formidable, the prisoners could not escape a thorough torturing.

The village meanwhile was restless. Squaws loitered in the cornfield looking down the river for the first sight of a canoe, old men walked back and forth to the stockade and peered into the distance. This would be a great homecoming. The Mohawk Valley was saved!

"Where are you going, Tekakwitha?" her aunts called as they panted up from the riverbank just in time to see her turn toward the forest. "They are coming, they are almost here!" they shouted. "The captives are singing."

As usual Tekakwitha wanted to flee, to seek some remote spot during the orgies of victory. In the quiet of the forest she felt less alone than when among her people at a time of celebration.

"The Algonquin again!" Arosen commented.

"You never did like us," Karitha added with an offended air.

"I don't like the scalps or the singing of the captives. It is horrible. And I don't want to watch the torment and the slow burning to death." Tekakwitha was more than usually vehement.

"That shows that you are no real Mohawk," Karitha said

with a tone of finality. "Such an insult! To go to the forest when our warriors have rid us of our enemies and are coming home in triumph!"

Tekakwitha retraced her steps and with her wonted docility remained with her aunts.

Cries of jubilation from the squaws welcomed the on-coming braves carrying their trophies, the finely painted scalps at the end of poles. Tekakwitha closed her eyes with a shudder; but she could not lock her ears against the grotesque singing of the captives. As the tragic procession passed her she met the anguished eyes of a Mohican squaw who staggered as though the child in her arms were too heavy a burden. The infant lay limp and Tekakwitha saw that it was dead. Later the rumor spread that the Blackrobe had baptized it while they were crossing a brook a few moments before the child died. Tekakwitha saw his tall figure among the captives and was comforted. He would tell them of Rawenniio and heaven. It would make their dying easier.

Days of torment for the Mohicans followed. Tekakwitha busied herself in the long house; but returning from the well one evening at dusk she could not avoid passing the scaffold. The fires were burning low. Temporarily the torturing was over and the slumping figures of the captives stood alone among the scalps of their countrymen. Suddenly there was a stir among them and from behind her Tekakwitha heard a voice with compassion in it bidding them to come down. The desolate group followed the Blackrobe into an empty cabin close at hand where he began to prepare them for death. He had instructed some of them during the journey and many had already asked for baptism.

The Mohawks, relaxed after the orgies of the day, were sitting about smoking their pipes; but some of the more curious followed the prisoners and stood near the cabin where they could hear the missionary speaking to them of eternal salvation. They shook their heads incredulously and looked at each other in surprise.

"See how he loves our enemies," one of them ventured.

"He ought to let them burn in hell," another interjected more fiercely.

"No," others interposed, "the Blackrobe did well. We should not carry vengeance beyond life."

Father Pierron overheard. "We must love our enemies," he said gently as he turned around, "with the love of Christ for us all." When he saw the crowd assembled, taking the Mohawk's words for a text he taught them with Christ's Sermon on the Mount.

"Our souls are immortal," he added, "and it is the Christian's duty to procure the happiness of heaven for all." The Mohawks were listening attentively. "In Paradise," he continued, "there is only one beautiful family, only one God who loves us with the same love and unites all our hearts in Himself."

The Mohawks drew a little closer. Tekakwitha had put down her pitcher and stood still. She was riveted as though listening to music.

Father Pierron concluded by telling them that God had shown His special love for the Mohawks in sending the Blackrobe to show them the way to heaven. The Blackrobe should do this because the Mohawks maintained him and allowed him to live in peace among them. At the end the Mohawks agreed that the priest did well to instruct the prisoners. Tekakwitha picked up her pitcher and thought of her inexorable uncle. Sadly and silently she returned to her pagan household.

Something was happening to the Mohawks. They had given the Blackrobe time to instruct the condemned Mohicans and under the influence of his words they no longer begrudged them happiness in the other world. Even after the priest had finished speaking they did not disperse, but stood by, nonplused, while a captive woman who had fallen upon her knees was offering a long prayer to Christ, imploring salvation.

All the prisoners desired baptism, and the Mohawks could not explain to themselves why torturing them and putting them to death had lost some of its savor. Instead, bravest of the Mohicans, a warrior who had killed many Iroquois, prayed in public and was baptized in their presence shortly before he died.

Father Pierron, ever since his arrival from Canada in 1667 as one of the peace messengers from the French, until his departure in 1671 to take charge of the mission on the St. Lawrence, was an influence in the Mohawk Valley which even the pagans could not ignore. Under his firm but gentle guidance a gradual veering toward Christianity was perceptible. More and more the people grew to respect and to trust him, and what pleased them especially, he entertained as well as instructed them. He painted pictures and invented games to convey the truths of Christianity, and he taught their children to read and write. Pagans and Christians alike were fascinated by his pictures of heaven with its many angels and hell with its multitude of devils. With zest they also played the new game of cards that he taught them, which he named: From Point to Point, that is: From Birth to Eternity. This was even more absorbing than their ancient game of Dish. All the forces of good and evil played a part in it; but Faith, Hope, and Charity were the trump cards and the virtues took the tricks.

And yet, many a lonely evening the Blackrobe knelt in the darkness with anguish in his soul. When weather permitted he went to every village in his province once a week; but although he might walk up and down the Mohawk Valley until he was spent, he could never reach all those who needed him. Never could he visit all the sick. Someone would die without baptism, and often, much too often, the villages rocked with debauches. Men, crazed with firewater, spread destruction and could easily put him to death at any time.

On the other hand, a spirit was astir against which all the buffetings of the angels of Satan were in vain. The blood of Jogues, of René Goupil, of the other martyrs, had sunk into this North American earth and its fruit must come. Amid these many crosscurrents Tekakwitha lived with busy hands and silent lips, and a deeper silence in her heart.

CHAPTER 13 The village of the Turtles was empty. Beyond the palisade a long, slow procession was disappearing into the woods. Torches flickered and flamed through the trees while the wailing of women came through the night, with the rise and fall of the chant for the dead. This was the concluding act of the most sacred celebration of the Iroquois, which took place every ten years when each separate nation had its own feast and gathered its dead to be buried in one common grave. With care and affection every family took its dead from their temporary resting places, covered them with handsome furs and hanging robes, carried them on their shoulders, every family to its cabin, and prepared a feast in their honor.

When these rites were over, the dead were taken in state and with precious gifts to the place of general interment. Solemnly the Mohawks surrounded the burial pit and many a weird and tragic demonstration of grief accompanied the ceremony. After the pit was filled and covered, the women trudged back and forth to place hampers of food upon it. According to Iroquois belief the soul of a person who had died hovered near the body until the Feast of the Dead. Only then did the spirit take its final journey to the other world.

Tekakwitha was there, richly dressed, wearing the elaborate wampum belt of a chieftain's daughter, her deerskin tunic, short skirt, leggings and moccasins, heavily beaded and embroidered with brightly colored porcupine quills. She was standing with Iowerano, Karitha, and Arosen; but behind them and a little apart, as was natural to her. She did not join in the loud laments; her eyes were fixed upon the burial pit.

All through the night, with her dead in the long house, she had lain sleepless upon her mat. It was her first Feast of the Dead and for a little while all that remained of her father, her mother, her little brother, had been with her in the cabin. No longer a child, she felt the pain of sudden realization, the emptiness that was, where they might have been. She had laid the fagots for the fire of last night, and sat with the others around the kettle; but something had happened within her. For years the strongest love that she knew had lain quietly folded as in the memory of a child. In the presence of her dead, a tragic reality had come close. At this touch of pain, love awakened and lived, a still white flame burning with the agony of loss.

The crowd was thinning around the burial pit; but Tekakwitha lingered, looking intently at the mounded grave laden with its gifts of food. Now, as her people said, the souls could travel over to the spirit world. At this moment she remembered the faces of the condemned Mohicans. She saw again the peace in their eyes that no torture could quench; for the Blackrobe had poured the water over their heads and promised them salvation, heaven, and happiness with Rawenniio.

"Hurry, Tekakwitha. What is the matter with you?" the voice of Karitha roused her. Slowly she followed, back to the village, into the long house and the dark.

Not only did the Feast of the Dead leave its impress upon Tekakwitha's inner life, but a dramatic incident during its progress brought consequences charged with significance. Father Pierron, now at Tionnontoguen, had been cordially invited to the celebration and took his place among the Mohawk dignitaries, with Tekakwitha's uncle and groups of chiefs and sachems of the Oneidas and the Onondagas. One of the latter rose for a speech and when he had finished, the Mohawk chiefs in turn recounted the principal fables and superstitions of their nation. But a sudden stir began with the men and continued among the women who stood near. They heard the Blackrobe's voice and he was trying to show them how absurd their fables were. One of the chiefs abruptly ordered him to be silent and immediately a bedlam of voices arose. Some found fault with the chief for his discourtesy, others upbraided the missionary for interfering and accused him of ridiculing their beliefs. "His mouth must be stopped at once!" an angry voice cried out.

Father Pierron was aware of his influence over the people and made immediate appeal to their love of fair play.

"Do you know," he said, addressing the offending chief, "that you have given me the keenest affront that I could have received? But who are you to order me to be silent, and am I here to obey you? If I had treated you thus in Quebec, would you not have cause to complain? In what have I spoken evil, that my mouth should be closed? And if I speak the truth, why are you not willing to hear?"

"It is the custom to keep up fables," the chief replied, with the edge gone from his voice.

"It is your custom to get intoxicated," the priest continued fearlessly. "Honestly, is it a good custom, and ought I approve it? It is your custom to violate every law of reason, and to live like the beasts; think you it is not my duty to reprove you for all these vices? And yet you impose silence upon me when I would speak to you. Is this reasonable?"

They could reach no agreement, so Father Pierron withdrew when the singing began, and joined a group of Onondagas, who received him with respect. When the ceremony of five hours was over, he went back to the village at once, leaving the Mohawks in the forest, and the rumor spread that he would return to Quebec. Alone in his cabin, the candle had nearly burnt itself out when someone lifted the bearskin curtain hesitantly. It was the chief who had caused the discord.

"My brother," he began, with a tone of apology, "up to this hour we have acted toward one another as the two best friends in the world. Tell me then, frankly," he said, placing his hand over his heart, "in what humor is your soul? They say that you are going to Quebec and will no more come to live with us. If this be so, I implore you not to get us into difficulty with Onnontio, the governor; for this would bring trouble upon yourself, if so many, both old and young, who greatly love and honor you, should for this reason receive ill-treatment. Tell me then, what is in your heart, and what are your sentiments?"

The priest was deeply touched, and although the chief's dramatic formality almost forced a smile, he assumed a serious manner which he seldom used.

"They have told you," he said, "that I have an irritated mind and a heart full of grief. This is true, and you know well that you are the cause. You have treated me with the greatest indignity. You have even presumed to impose silence when I would speak of the Faith, which is the thing of all else, as you know, that I have most at heart. Did it not confuse you to see me so well received by the Onondagas whom I did not know, driven out by those who professed to be my friends?"

"My brother," the chief replied humbly, "I see what is at the bottom of this quarrel; it is that we are not yet Christians. But if you will leave this important affair to me, I promise you success. This is what you must do: first convoke a council, and then, having given three belts to our three families, with each present speak out your mind. After this leave me to act, and I trust all will go well."

It did. With the usual ceremony that attended all the formal functions of the Iroquois the grandees of the Mohawk nation assembled in Father Pierron's cabin; but Tekakwitha's uncle was not among them. The Blackrobe spoke and was greeted with cries of applause. He presented a fathom of wampum and said: "My brother, if it is true that you are willing to hear me, there is my voice, which warns you and entreats you wholly to renounce Aireskoi, and never speak to him, but to adore the true God and follow His law." He threw down his second gift of wampum with the plea that the medicine men no longer invoke demons for the cure of diseases, but use natural remedies. At this they applauded again and again and even the medicine men showed their good will. The third piece of wampum, to destroy the superstition associated with their dances, was received with acclaim.

Some days later the council fires burned bright and even a delegation of Onondagas had come to join in the session. After the Blackrobe had spoken, their chief, Garacontié, raised a compelling voice:

"Take his word," he enjoined them, "for he has sacrificed all for you." Like a fresh wind a new spirit shook some of the villages into action. The sorcerers threw their turtle-shell rattles into the fire, the women no longer called the medicine men for the cure of diseases, and the people stopped all dances of which the Blackrobe did not approve.

This revolutionizing movement had also its more affirmative side; for the oyanders, as the Iroquois called their nobles, began to bring their young people in crowds to be instructed by the missionary. But Father Pierron was not carried away, even by this overwhelming success. The glow that burned in his eyes at the moment of his first arrival was a steady light. The apparent hopelessness of his task at the beginning, the failures, the occasional hostility, had not snuffed it; nor did this latest and bewildering success augment it. In a letter to his superior at this climactic period of his ministry, he wrote: "Their natural inconstancy still divides my heart between fear and joy."

Iowerano looked with a sullen eye upon the enthusiasm around him. The new spirit abroad in the valley was becoming infectious and often his glance was full of suspicion and uneasiness as it fell upon Tekakwitha; but she continued to remain quietly in the lodge. Nevertheless she was far from asleep in her corner. Cries from the outside: "Hail to Rawenniio! Down with sorcery! Down with Aireskoi!" reached her attentive ears. A squaw of the long house had told her that the Great Spirit was now to be worshiped by all. The deep pain left in her heart by the Feast of the Dead began to feel a touch of healing and the empty yearning for her Christian mother was being filled by a hope that was new. Despite the eyes of Iowerano, despite the nagging and the chatter of Karitha and Arosen, a loveliness as of the dawn was spreading over the silent, struggling world within her, coming from the light of a Presence, Rawenniio in the land of the Mohawks!

CHAPTER 14 "What are you two women talking about, with your heads together as though no one should hear?" Iowerano asked good-humoredly, throwing himself down beside a newly-made fire.

"Tekakwitha," both his wife and his sister answered in one breath. "We were saying that it is time for her to marry."

The chief nodded in approval. "I have been thinking of her. She will make a desirable wife, a docile and a useful one."

"She is not beautiful," Karitha interposed. "We had better be quick about it or she will stay on our hands, and that would be a disgrace as well as a nuisance."

"But she is clever," Iowerano defended, "and timid as she is, she has a ready wit and is always cheerful, even gay."

"Of course you never see any faults in her," Karitha complained.

"I don't see what more you could expect of her. She knows more than any of the other Iroquois girls. She not only embroiders the elk and the deerskin delicately with beads and porcupine quills and makes burden straps for the women, but her wampum belts are always the most beautiful, and the old men like to wear them for the affairs of the nation."

"Every girl ought to be able to do that if she is well taught," Karitha said with a toss of the head. But Iowerano was not to be silenced. He was in a mood of enthusiasm and talked much more than was usual with him.

"But every girl cannot make nets, and buckets for drawing water, or such neatly braided mats from bark; nor do they make pestles or prepare the poles for hanging the ears of corn. She is not strong. That, you know; but she is always the first at work and the last to take a holiday — and she never gads about," he added pointedly.

For once Karitha had nothing to say in reply. Arosen meantime was looking admiringly at her brother.

"It will be easy," she said, "to find a strong young hunter for her. Any brave would be glad to live in the lodge of the leading chief of Gandawagué." Iowerano looked pleased, and puffed at his pipe.

"Then there will always be plenty of game brought to the lodge for food, and a good supply of furs to exchange at Albany for the goods of the cloth workers," he added contentedly. "But where is Tekakwitha?"

"She is out pounding the corn," Karitha volunteered.

"Here I am!" Tekakwitha called brightly, slipping in from one side of the bearskin curtain, a large bowl of ground maize in her arms. She came at once toward the fire and began to prepare the cornmeal for the sagamite.

"Get out your prettiest moccasins, Tekakwitha, and the ribbons for your hair," said Karitha smiling. "We are going to the feast this evening, and you must be with us."

Tekakwitha continued with her cooking. Her back was turned, so no one saw the shadow that crossed her face; but with her usual docility she agreed and said no more about it.

A few years ago she had often passed the time stringing beads for ornaments. She was adept at fashioning ribbons from eel skins or from strong pieces of bark and reddening them with paste from the sturgeon. She wore these things and adorned herself with beads, earrings, and the usual finery, to please her aunts. She was accustomed to obey; but now their demands were growing. She was no longer permitted to spend time in the way that pleased her best and she sensed the conflict to come. Repeatedly they were insisting upon her presence at dances and feasts where they tried to arouse her interest in some young brave or another. The efforts to satisfy the wishes of her family caused her acute suffering. Her shyness increased if possible, with the pressure put upon it and the modesty that was her native endowment shrank from the uncouth and often ribald scenes that she was forced to witness.

As she sat between her aunts at this feast which she had been forced to attend, she was thinking her own thoughts, and they wandered far from all that was going on about her.

"Look!" Karitha prodded. "That is Red Eagle, the best dancer in the village, and a famous hunter. See how the girls are trying to attract his attention! But his eyes are on you, Tekakwitha."

"He is looking at my disfigured face," the girl told herself in an agony of embarrassment.

If only she might withdraw from all questioning eyes! Something else, however, lay deeper than any personal humiliation. Despite her patience, in defiance of her gentleness, she could not hide from herself an aversion that was fundamental, a disgust with the life around her, although it was the environment into which she was born.

Perhaps she did not realize that scarcely a generation ago, another Indian girl had inwardly resisted these same surroundings, and with all the forces of her soul. Nearly two centuries would pass before the Curé of Ars was to say: "Virtue passes easily from the hearts of mothers into the hearts of children." Had Tekakwitha been a Christian she might have felt that Kahenta had sown a seed and was watching over its growth.

As for Red Eagle, she had seen him not long ago and she shrank from the thought of him. On that occasion also, he had been a leader, a leader in the torturing of the Mohicans. With growing distaste she endured the whisperings of her aunts:

"Is Two Feathers not a handsome brave?"

"Which one is he?" Tekakwitha asked indifferently.

"I never saw such a girl!" Karitha exclaimed impatiently.

"Tekakwitha, you are stupid," Arosen added. "Everyone knows Two Feathers, the bravest of our young warriors. There he is, speaking to your uncle."

Again Tekakwitha shuddered. A row of scalps was dangling from his belt.

"She is queer!" Arosen commented when the two women were alone.

"She is like her mother."

"The worse for her!" Karitha said and looked her disgust.

"Her Algonquin origin must be to blame for her lack of interest in our Mohawk customs. Just look at her feet. She even walks like an Algonquin."

"You are right, Karitha. The Mohawks do not turn their feet inward like other Indians do," Arosen added proudly.

"But the Algonquins are gentle and yielding," said Karitha hopefully.

"Tekakwitha is obedient. She will yield."

The chief overheard and concluded the conversation: "Tekakwitha must yield," he said, and his heavy jaws snapped shut.

CHAPTER 15 Karitha felt secure in the thought that Iowerano's severity would finally prevail over Tekakwitha's unprecedented resistance. The wish not to marry was beyond the understanding of a Mohawk. For the present, cajolery would serve the purpose better than force. Apparently Red Eagle and Two Feathers had made no impression upon Tekakwitha. Ingratiatingly Karitha and Arosen introduced the names of other eligible braves into the daily conversation, hoping to rouse their niece out of her indifference.

"Ah! Tekakwitha is embroidering her wedding garments," Arosen would say teasingly when the girl sat quietly in a corner, bending over her embroidery.

"What handsome wampum belts her husband will wear!" Karitha added slyly. At that the chief looked pleased. "I shall have a strong brave to help me bring in the game and the furs," he said, puffing contentedly at his pipe. "Then I can take it easy."

Tekakwitha looked up with the smile that covered even her disfigurement with charm. "Really, I have no desire to marry," she said in her most amiable manner. "And I am still much too young."

"Perhaps that is true," the chief conceded.

"That will soon be remedied." Karitha laughed. "But who

ever heard of a girl not wanting to marry! Do you intend to disgrace us?"

They did however seem to accept her youth as an excuse for postponement; for they made no further allusions to marriage, and Tekakwitha was permitted to resume her daily tasks unmolested.

Meanwhile an undercurrent of change was becoming more and more perceptible in the village. In 1669 Father Boniface, another young Jesuit whom the lure of the North American missions had drawn from his home in France, arrived in Canada and was sent at once to the Mohawk Valley to assume some of the burdens that had grown too heavy for Father Pierron to carry alone. The latter was now stationed at Tionnontoguen, the castle of the Wolves, where he had replaced Father Frémin in 1668; so Father Boniface went to the people of Gandawagué, and in 1670 established for them a mission of their own.

The little bark chapel, St. Peter's, soon became a stronghold in the bitter struggle between the forces of good and evil, and at the same time a mainspring from which many life-giving impulses would flow. Nevertheless despite the tireless labors and the ingenuity of Father Boniface, the mission was only a partial success. He came into the tumult of intermittent war between Indian nations. Mohawks and Mohicans were still devouring one another. Although the demon Aireskoi had fallen from his former dominating position, life was still predominantly pagan and the next step, the implanting of Christian truth, was beset with hazards that seemed insurmountable.

But Canada was drawing closer and was beginning to play a new and telling part in the spiritual drama. Before the end of 1670 the Mohawk Valley was startled by the news that in

June the famous Onondaga chief, Garacontié, had been baptized in Quebec. A little French settlement, Laprairie de la Madeleine, was also drawing attention to the south bank of the St. Lawrence where a new village for Christian Indians had sprung up in 1667. It began with the temporary stay of several Oneidas and Mohawks who had been on a visit to Montreal and Quebec and were attracted to the spot by Father Raffeix who had built a chapel there. This was the Blackrobe who had accompanied both de Courcelle and de Tracy's expeditions to the Mohawk Valley. At first the Indians came out of curiosity or for temporary shelter, then settled with their families and friends until they formed a village of Christian Indians destined to become a meeting place for converts from all five nations of the Iroquois. The French governor encouraged the project and a large tract was given to the Jesuits, which the Canadians called St.-François-Xavier-des-Prés, and which was the beginning of the mission which has continued to exist down to the present day. Later the settlement moved close to the Lachine Rapids which gave it the name of St.-François-Xavier-du-Sault, in Indian called Caughnawaga, that is to say at the Rapids, the same name as that of transplanted Gandawagué in the Mohawk Valley.

All those who lived at the mission had to renounce first of all the idolatry of dreams, second the exchange of wives — a custom which had been in vogue at feasts — and third drunkenness. Anyone who relapsed was expelled by the chiefs whom the Indians chose from among the more fervent Christians and who usually had been of high rank in their own country. Some of them were famous in the history of the time and brought additional honor upon the settlement, which soon became known among the Indians at large as the Praying Castle on the St. Lawrence.

Meantime, under the direction of the intrepid Father Boniface, the Christian Indians of Gandawagué in the Mohawk Valley were learning to pray and to sing. Regularly as in the well-ordered Catholic families of France, the Christian Indian families of St. Peter's mission gathered for morning and evening prayers, ending with the singing of hymns in Iroquois. This practice soon revealed the special talent for music and singing which the Iroquois possess. Even the children, only seven or eight years old, formed a choir of their own.

For a time a Pentecostal wind seemed to be blowing over Gandawagué bringing a complete transformation. Old Christians regained their fervor, and daily the number of conversions increased. Every Saturday evening the statue of Notre Dame de Foy, which had been brought from Tionnontoguen, was uncovered and left exposed throughout Sunday for the veneration of the Christians who assembled three times during the day to pray the rosary.

Father Boniface was constantly finding new ways of stimulating the devotion of his converts. For them he revived the ancient ceremony — common in seventeenth-century France — of the blessed bread, and this aboriginal group gathered every Sunday in the cabin of some devout squaw to celebrate this primitive love feast of the earliest Christians. Like children of one family, those who had once feasted on human flesh partook of the blessed bread together, as of the gift of their common Father. The woman who provided it always served a light repast at the same time, with the prayer before and after meals.

But it was the following Christmas that brought their Faith home to them in the most appealing manner; for Father Boniface had planned a surprise. In a corner of the chapel, aglow with lights and adorned with evergreens, the stable of Bethlehem stood under hovering angels. A beautiful Christ Child lay in His crib with His Mother kneeling beside Him, St. Joseph watching over them, and hesitant shepherds coming with their sheep. Like the shepherds, the timid Indians came. All day long they stole silently in and out with awe upon their faces while Father Boniface told and retold the wondrous story.

Outside in the snow the crowd stood and waited, looking with interest up at the cross, an object of terror in René Goupil's time; but now at last a familiar sign. The pagans too were curious. They came, marveled, and went away pleased. This was a language all could understand: a scanty shelter against the cold, a bed of straw, a child with its mother. The Lady's shawl was the blue of the summer sky. The man wore brown, the color of the earth and the deerskin.

Tekakwitha with her aunts and Ennita, her adopted sister, also stood in the snow and waited. Anastasia was there, beside the relatives of the Great Mohawk, Kryn, and the wife of Kryn with sorrow in her eyes. Together they moved into the candlelight and stood about the crib while the Blackrobe told the story. Tekakwitha saw all and heard all; but went away in silence.

Something strange yet dimly recognized stirred in her heart as the children's voices followed her out into the cold:

> "Within a lodge of broken bark
> The tender Babe was found;
> A ragged robe of rabbit skin
> Enwrapped His beauty round."

She lost the thread with the crunching of the snow under

many feet. Then it came again, faintly, as they left the chapel farther behind:

> "While chiefs from far before Him knelt
> With gifts of fox and beaver pelt. . . ."

The wife of Kryn remained behind, kneeling among the Christians who, despite the cold, spent the feast in song and prayer, remaining longer than usual. So tender was their devotion to this mystery and their love for the Christmas carols that the Blackrobe permitted them to continue singing them until Easter.

Darkness fell early on that Christmas day of 1672, and the bitter cold penetrated the little bark chapel. The lights were still burning about the crib, a wisp of incense hung poised, then disappeared. The singing was over; but its echoes lingered in the ears of Father Boniface. His heart gave thanks as he looked at the floor and saw the trodden snow, carried in by thronging feet. The chapel was empty, but for one kneeling figure. "It is the wife of Kryn!" Father Boniface said to himself. "May the Mother of the Christ Child comfort her!" He knelt again. In silence he would pray with her. She must be left undisturbed a few moments longer. She was one of his most fervent converts and had openly declared herself a Christian, despite the fact that most of her associations were pagan, and her husband Kryn, the conqueror of the Mohicans, stood high in the councils of the village. They had one child, "an only daughter" as the letters of the Jesuits relate, "whose bright disposition made all in the town love her." Difficulties arose between husband and wife, and six months after the latter's conversion Kryn deserted her and went on a long journey from which he had not returned.

Soon after his departure the daughter died. The bereft mother was blamed on all sides. Her pagan friends, still numerous, told her that she should not have adopted the strange customs of the Blackrobes, and that this was the reason for Kryn's desertion. It was why the child had died. But under the pitiless lashing of tongues the woman's faith stood firm and in desolation her fervor grew.

She raised her eyes at last. The candles at the crib had almost burned out and shadows quivered over the darkening stable. The Blackrobe was standing beside her.

"It is too cold for you, my daughter."

The flicker of a smile brightened in her heavy eyes.

"I do not feel it, Father."

"This is a happy Christmas for your little one. She is with the Christ Child," he said gently.

"Yes, Father, I know."

"Is there news of Kryn?"

"None, Father."

"It will come."

Father Boniface walked with her down the little aisle.

"Are your friends still making you suffer?"

"It does not matter any more," the woman whispered.

" 'Blessed are they,' " the priest said softly, " 'that suffer persecution for justice' sake; for theirs is the kingdom of heaven.' That is the Christ Child's answer."

The woman smiled gratefully and walked out into the snow that lay glittering in the light of early stars.

Still deeper lay the snow in the forests of Canada and strong winds were sweeping over the frozen St. Lawrence, beating against a tall figure on snowshoes, breasting its way toward a settlement close to the shore. It was good after the long journey and many days of hunting in the forest to stumble upon this village, the name of which he could not even guess; for the country was strange to him and he had lost his way innumerable times.

It was the season of the winter hunt. The village must be nearly empty. Nevertheless a muffled figure was walking toward him and he thought he heard a voice coming through the whistling wind. He could scarcely believe it, but someone was calling him by name.

"Kryn! What a surprise! Welcome to Laprairie!"

A responsive warmth kindled in the eyes of the Mohawk as he recognized the Blackrobe, Father Frémin, who with Fathers Bruyas and Pierron had come to the Mohawks in 1667 in fulfillment of peace conditions with the French, after de Tracy's campaign. He had remembered and respected this Blackrobe ever since the latter's short stay in Gandawagué on his way to the capital at Tionnontoguen. Gratefully Kryn followed his host into the bark cabin, warmed himself at his fire, and shared his sagamite. As he lay wrapped in a bearskin on the mat made ready for him, he almost smiled into the darkness at the humor of the situation. The Great Mohawk in the Praying Castle! And glad to be there!

CHAPTER 16 Quietly and uncon-
cerned, Tekakwitha sat by the fire in her appointed lodge
seat. Her uncle tugged at his pipe, his eyes fixed upon the
bearskin curtain. Her aunts bustled about restlessly with an
air of suspense, turning their heads from time to time, Karitha
to look appraisingly at her unsuspecting niece, Arosen
apparently alert for the first sign of the awaited guests. They
must be people of unusual consequence. The thought flitted
through Tekakwitha's mind; but she was not curious, though
their names had not been disclosed. Visitors were frequent in
the chief's long house and Tekakwitha was often bidden to
wear her best attire.

This evening, however, Karitha had dressed her hair with
more than usual attention and had wound more elaborate
beads into her long black braid. The firelight played fitfully
over her skirt, her leggings and moccasins, richly embroidered
with procupine quills in pink and green. Strands of wampum
beads woven into curious devices hung about her neck and
the long girdle trailing on the ground beside her, was fit
for a princess. Everything was in readiness, everyone was
waiting; but where were the guests?

As if in answer to the unspoken question, the bearskin
curtain moved and a young brave dressed as for a holiday
appeared, followed by his relatives. He was tall as the tallest

of the Mohawks and his step was quick and assured. It was not Red Eagle, not Two Feathers. Tekakwitha dimly remembered having seen him; but she did not know his name. Her family stepped forward to receive the guests; but the eyes of the young brave sought the girl and they brightened at sight of her elegant attire. She looked that which she was, the daughter of a chief. Tekakwitha found herself wishing that Ennita was there. Though adopted in name, the older girl was not an intimate part of the family and was often away; but Tekakwitha missed her quiet sympathy.

Without a word, at a sign from Karitha the young brave strode over to where Tekakwitha was sitting and took his place beside her. Her unconcern was startled into bewilderment. She had not noticed the lavish gift of beaver furs that preceded his arrival. Her face flushed deeply; but Karitha was prompt, and without giving her time to think, bade her present the bowl of sagamite. Then she knew. It was the Mohawk marriage rite. If she complied, the man beside her would be her accepted husband. Again the hot blood mounted to her cheeks and beat in her ears like the sound of rushing waters. Everyone was looking at her, smiling expectantly. One short moment, an agony of suspense, and the destiny of a lifetime hanging upon it! She rose abruptly and was gone.

All the wildness, all the shyness of the hunted thing, all the agility, the intrepidity of the Indian that she was, pressed her into headlong flight and the half blind eyes strained to their feeble utmost. Down the slope she fled, stumbling, catching herself, falling, hiding for a moment, running again, carried on by something insistent, fundamental, immediate as her own being. She did not know what it was; but it moved her, not toward something but away, away from something that for some inexplicable reason would destroy her. Breathlessly she reached the fields on the riverbank and crouched among the growing things, trembling in every fiber of her body, praying with all the unexplored powers of her soul to Rawenniio, the God of the Blackrobes and of her mother, Kahenta.

The night seemed waiting with her, the river barely rippled in the windless air. The silence was a presence and her friend until the angry voices of her aunts tore it from her. She wanted to shrink into the earth; but the ground was white with moonlight and they found her.

"Tekakwitha, come back, come back at once. You are a wicked girl. You will bring shame upon us all. Your uncle will punish you severely."

The girl shrank from them and turned her face away. They clutched her arms, they tried to pull at her girdle; but something strong had come into her and they knew that force was in vain.

"We have made excuses," they urged in a changed tone. "You were taken by surprise. You were frightened. Come with us and all will yet be well."

"No," she said, and her voice was firm. "I will not set foot in the cabin until he has gone."

Even Karitha almost lost the power of speech; but her eyes blazed. Between them they dragged her back, up the hill and toward the cabin. She was too slight to resist the pull upon her arms, now that they knew she was beyond persuasion.

At the door of the long house she paused. Involuntarily they paused with her.

"Please, no farther. I will not go in."

They had felt her straighten and there was a quality in her voice that forbade further violence.

The brave had gone. The food was untasted and the chief, with fury in his eyes, sat alone. At sight of Tekakwitha he rose and stormed toward her.

"You dare to defy me!" he thundered, shaking his fist in her face, "me who have been a father to you?"

"She's an ungrateful girl," Karitha screamed.

"Are you crazy, Tekakwitha?" Arosen interrupted. "Such a handsome brave as Silver Arrow!"

"Be quiet, women," ordered Iowerano. "Leave her to me. I'll teach her to obey."

"I am sorry to displease you, my Father." Tekakwitha's voice was gentle. "But you leave me no choice. You gave me no warning and I could not take Silver Arrow for a husband."

"Could not take Silver Arrow!" Iowerano laughed loud in mockery. "And who do you think you are? If it were not for me Silver Arrow would not even look at a girl like you. And you have insulted him. Do you understand what a terrible thing you have done? And what is more, you are insulting your forebears, your traditions, the customs of our tribe. Every Indian girl must marry when the time comes or she is a disgrace to herself and to her people."

Tekakwitha did not flinch before this onslaught. When Iowerano stopped for sheer want of breath she said:

"I do not mean to offend you or anyone, my Father. I shall continue to serve you gladly and faithfully; but I do not wish to marry. Please leave me this freedom."

Again the women protested with a torrent of words.

"Be still, squaws," the chief shouted. "Tekakwitha will come to her senses. She will not dare to humiliate us again."

He glared at the girl and the look in her eyes whipped him to new fury. Something that he recognized was burning in them. Confronting him was a Mohawk, indomitable as he.

"Go to bed!" he shouted. "I do not want to see your face."

The night was long for Tekakwitha lying wakeful upon her mat. All the deeper forces within her were stirred to a tumult that beat against the closed doors of her habitual obedience; and the doors were being forced to open. What was this wild cry for freedom, breaking forth within her? Why this fierce resistance to the customs of her race? It had always been easy for her to obey when a duty was in question, and giving pleasure to others was never irksome. She looked back upon her behavior on this fateful evening, her sudden, precipitous flight, her disregard of consequences. It seemed like that of another person, and yet that other person was more intimately herself than was the Indian girl of every day, who carried water, gathered wood, and lit the fires for the household.

But for the conviction that she was the inferior of everyone, Kateri had never been preoccupied with herself. This discovery of her personality almost dismayed her. Child of a primitive race as she was, her mind obviously did not follow the devious ways of self-analysis. She was unaware of complexes. She did not know personality or individuality by name; but she was coming to grips with the thing that it was and it shook her with its elemental power. Nevertheless it did not tear her apart. With the power born of a strong inner life she gathered her forces into a focal point of quiet endurance.

Heavy-eyed, she rose to her daily tasks and to the sullen silence that she encountered at every turn. Her uncle ignored her, her aunts lost no opportunity to make her feel her utter disgrace. From time to time a look of cunning stole into Karitha's eyes. For her the matter was far from finished. There were other eligible braves in Gandawagué. The next time would find Tekakwitha more receptive. They would wear down her resistance. They would make a slave of her, and let her know what it meant to defy them.

They did it and she rose to the test as always. This attitude on the part of her family continued and the monotonous life went on until late one summer afternoon when, quite casually Iowerano brought Tiger Eye, a visiting Iroquois of the Onondaga tribe, home with him. Upon his arrival the unsuspecting brave was given to understand that he had come for Tekakwitha; but experience had made her wary. Just as casually she picked up her burden strap and disappeared.

Not long afterward Green Turtle came to the lodge. From behind the long house where she was pounding the maize, Tekakwitha saw him, dropped her pestle, and fled into the forest. The quiet trees comforted her and filled her own silence with added strength and reassurance. Stillness was a wondrous thing. Even the unrelenting silence of her family was a protection from something more unbearable. It met her, as usual, upon her return, hours later. Too proud to admit defeat by an expression of anger, her uncle and her aunts gave no sign of having noticed her absence. They were losing this wordless battle of wits. No matter how embarrassing the position into which they tried to place her, Tekakwitha remained unruffled, apparently oblivious of their designs, but constantly defeating them.

In desperation they concentrated all their cunning upon a final effort. Iowerano had recently seen White Lightning, an eligible young hunter from the castle of the Bears, and enlisted his interest in Tekakwitha. The aunts roused themselves to a semblance of enthusiasm. If all went well he would bring great honor to their lodge. They received him with every ceremony of welcome; but while they were exchanging courtesies, Tekakwitha fled and hid herself behind a case of Indian corn standing at the rear of a neighboring long house. This time they did not find her and she was left to tremble in the loneliness of her thoughts. All that she was had driven her to this renewed decision, unheard of, incomprehensible to the Mohawk. Would the struggle never end?

Life lay before her an empty space; yet somehow there was a strange light upon it, something like a promise, felt rather than understood. It was something that broke through the distaste, the daily drudgery, that gave her the gift of laughter, that formed inner patterns for the designs that her fingers fashioned. It was something that kindled within her when the birds called and the chestnuts blossomed, when the autumn woods turned red.

Behind the packed corn Tekakwitha shivered, though the air was mild. The urge to flee was upon her — down the speeding river, through the trees, along the path of the deer. Should she seek shelter with Anastasia? Should she go to the wife of Kryn? Should she — her timidity drew her back from the very thought — should she beg protection from the Blackrobe?

The urge had spent itself. The trembling stopped. Slowly, steadily, she groped her way back to the long house.

CHAPTER 17   In the Valley of the Mohawks the corn was ripe. Screams of laughter and the singing of many voices flung back their echoes, doubly vibrant in the liquid air. The Mohawk girls were at their favorite occupation, husking ears of corn, throwing them into heaps, braiding them into bunches of twenty to be hung up and dried. On the outskirts of the group the older squaws urged them on with jests and laughter. Warriors and old men, scorning to participate in the frolic, sat at one side smoking their pipes undisturbed.

Gaily the young squaws tossed the ears to each other, with eyes fixed keenly upon every ear. In the midst of them Tekakwitha sat with a bright red ear in her hand, blushing at their peals of laughter and laughing merrily with them. The red ear! Sign of an admirer!

"It is Silver Arrow!" shouted Kaneka who sat directly opposite. "There he is," they all sang out together, pointing to the red ear. "See, he has come to woo you again!"

At first Tekakwitha felt like running away; but instead she made a playful gesture of throwing the ear of corn at Kaneka. Fun loving herself, she kept a close watch and caught Kaneka unsheathing a crooked ear that looked like a queer little bent man. It was the Wagenin of Indian lore, the little corn thief. Kaneka bit her lip, but had to smile in spite of herself while she tried to hide the crooked ear under her hand.

"Wagenin! Wagenin!" Tekakwitha sang out gleefully, "Wagenin Painosaid!" Quickly the others took up the song: "The little old corn thief, walker at night!"

Then all together, with the word Wagenin they began the chorus of the Algonquin corn song that the Mohawks had learned from their captives.

The laugh was now on the other girl. They recited the words, stanza after stanza, alternating between the singing of the chorus and the comic gestures. Tekakwitha sang with the others, her good humor unimpaired. She did not mind the teasing. Her wish to remain unmarried was no longer a secret and the girls often twitted her about it; but without a hint of malice, for they always enjoyed her company and especially her ready wit.

Even her family now left her in peace after a year of storms; but the persecution had been bitter. When coaxing and trickery failed, they had resorted to violence, treating her not only as a servant but a slave, forcing her to do everything that was repulsive or painful, putting a malignant interpretation upon her most innocent actions. They reproached her continually for her lack of attachment to her relatives, accused her of stupidity, of uncouth manners, and attributed everything to a hatred for the Iroquois, due to her Algonquin heritage.

Tekakwitha had always preferred to suffer rather than to cause others pain. Her unwearying patience under this domestic trial, her amiability, the fine balance between firmness and gentleness that was in her character gradually softened the hearts of her relatives and they became kind to her again. Besides, Ennita, the adopted daughter, had been a disappointment to them. She had married Onas, an excellent huntsman, but a Christian. Ennita herself was now a neophyte and no longer lived in the long house.

"The work of the Blackrobe, Boniface!" Iowerano muttered, with a dangerous look in his eyes.

He was growing more and more bitter against the teaching of the missionaries to which the heart and mind of Tekakwitha were invisibly opening. Little did he suspect that often in the semidarkness she lingered near the bark chapel listening to the singing and to the rise and fall of voices praying the rosary together. Sometimes she caught a few of the words and wondered. Were they speaking to the lovely Lady who knelt in the stable at Christmas time?

CHAPTER 18 Despite the labors of
Father Boniface the work of the mission was not a complete
success. The English had made peace between the Mohicans
and the Mohawks and the latter were purchasing liquor
freely at Fort Orange and carrying it in kegs to the fishing
villages. Drunkenness grew apace and caused severe illness
among the Mohawks, a quick, fatal fever that placed added
burdens upon the already overworked Jesuits of the region
through the winter of 1672–73.

Meantime the snows melted, the Mohawk River had
thrown off its weight of ice, and the valley was budding in
the April sunshine. For the first time, in the year 1673, a
strange canoe came skimming up the river and stopped at
Gandawagué. At sight of the tall figure hurrying up the
slope a cry of recognition roused the whole village to shouts
of welcome. Only the Great Mohawk could inspire such
tumultuous enthusiasm.

Alone in her cabin, the wife of Kryn heard and dropped
to her knees, the sadness gone from her face. It was a
different Kryn who returned to her. Canada had won his
affections and made a Christian of him. He had come for
his wife and he promised her that in the Christian village
of Laprairie they would find a happier home. The Mohawks
still regarded him as their national hero and he had a large

following among them. With apostolic zeal he used the time of his visit to proclaim his newly found Faith. The people gathered to listen, and when he told them that he was determined to renounce everything that could draw him back to the old life, not a single voice was raised in opposition. Fearlessly and publicly he offered to lead all those who were willing to follow him to Laprairie.

On the day of his departure at dawn, a loud call shook the sleeping village. Everyone knew it, the voice of the Great Mohawk that had so often summoned them to battle. An enthusiastic gathering responded; but, as Kryn announced, the rallying cry was only for Christians or for those who meant to be baptized. Between thirty and forty, after hurried farewells, left their homes and followed him. Among them were Onas and Ennita.

In the long house of the chief the women were astir. Karitha and Arosen, overcome by curiosity, wanted to run out to the square at once.

"Stay where you are, squaws!" thundered the chief. "Kryn has lost his senses." And he shook both fists in futile fury. The exodus did not end with the departure of Kryn. Father Boniface, whose health had been failing, felt the need of returning to Canada, and for a long time he had wished to remove his neophytes from the temptations surrounding them, to a place of greater security. In the June of 1673 he left for the Christian community at Laprairie, taking many converts with him and one Christian of long standing, Anastasia Tegonhatsihongo.

Anastasia had often seen a Blackrobe come and go, in earlier, more dangerous days. The fiber of her faith was strong and had survived many a testing; but she was tired of uncertainties, tired of the revolting scenes around her, and she longed for a place of peace. Tekakwitha stood beside her on the riverbank while the canoes were preparing to leave. She could not speak; but the feel of the desert was upon her. With Anastasia went her childhood and the one voice that spoke to her of Kahenta. When the last canoe had slipped into the enfolding hills Tekakwitha fled, far into the depths of the forest.

CHAPTER 19

In the same year of 1673, the Dutch had regained the province; but in 1674 Albany was again in the power of the English. Throughout this time Tekakwitha's uncle maintained his association with the Dutch. He was enraged at the departure of Kryn and of Father Boniface with so many of his people and he accused Father Bruyas, superior of the Jesuits in the Mohawk Valley, of breaking up the nation. He blamed Kryn most of all; and the conversion of Assendase, a prominent old chief of Tionnontoguen, the capital, aroused him to further hostility.

In 1675 Father James de Lamberville, who had come from France to Canada as a missionary in 1672 was sent to Gandawagué to replace Father Boniface and to take charge also of Andagoron, which had moved to the north side of the river. One day, not long after his arrival, he was walking among the cabins of Gandawagué in the quiet of early afternoon. It was his usual time, while the others were in the cornfields, to visit the old and the sick.

It did not take him long to know his sparse little flock, since the majority of Christians had gone to Canada; but he looked with the interest of the newcomer at every cabin in order to identify its occupants. He passed close to the doorway of the chief's long house; but there, he knew he must not enter. He was well aware of Iowerano's antagonism to the French from Montreal, and of his special enmity toward the Blackrobe.

Far back in a shadowed corner of the lodge Tekakwitha sat, and a few old squaws had strayed in to keep her company. A hoe had injured her foot and she was unable to go to the field. She saw the Blackrobe pass, since the curtain was partially withdrawn to admit the light, and the weariness of waiting was in her eyes. He passed without turning his head; but he had not gone many steps before he stood still. Something unaccountable was urging him to turn back and enter that forbidding cabin. Disturbed and hesitant, he stood for a moment at the open doorway. Tekakwitha looked up at the sudden shadow and saw him in the sunlight, a tall figure in a long black habit, a crucifix at the girdle. With a quick movement she limped to her feet. "Raquenee!" — "Father!" It was a cry of joy.

The missionary found it difficult to speak. He did not know what he had expected to encounter. Surely not the warmth of such a greeting from this pagan girl whom he had seen wrapped in her red shawl, walking like a wraith through the twilight. But Tekakwitha's words came quickly. Her heart was unsealed at last, and from out the long garnered riches of her solitude, desire leaped like a fountain at springtime. She could not conceal her joy. Even the presence of the three listening women did not deter her from telling the priest how she had wished to speak but did not dare to go and seek him. The longing for the Faith of her mother was growing within her. The obstacles were great; but she would disregard them now.

Father de Lamberville's keen spiritual vision told him at once that he had found a treasure. He studied the look upon

her face while she spoke; it was modest, yet resolute. The
flash of ardor and courage had covered every hint of blind-
ness in her eyes. He saw that here would be no neophyte
of average type. His own burning zeal rose to the challenge
and he began at once, during this first visit, to give her
some instruction. He found her unbelievably ready and responsive, tutored as it were, from within. Later he confided
to a fellow Jesuit that he perceived from the first interview,
that God had great designs upon this soul. He would nevertheless take all the usual precautions and not hasten her
baptism.

When Tekakwitha recovered from her accident she began
at once to attend morning and evening prayers, telling her
family frankly that she was going to St. Peter's Chapel. To
her surprise they offered no opposition. The people wondered
at this and came to the conclusion that it was due to the
fact that they had often seen Kahenta at her prayers and
therefore it was nothing new to them.

Tekakwitha spent the winter in preparation for baptism.
A new light was dawning and she found answer upon
answer to the mute questionings within her. She was entirely
an Indian, yet could not live like one. On the surface perhaps, in the lesser affairs of life; but not wholeheartedly,
with the total consent of her being. She lived among her
people, an alien to the inner drives that dominated them.
And yet, she was conscious of forces within her, strong, over-
powering ones. She had found an object at last upon which
to expend them.

She who felt herself so helpless, so inferior, so unattractive,
was coming upon something worth while that she could do,
and a Love that could fill her, fashion her, and comfort her.

Father de Lamberville meantime was following the usual

course of the missionaries, to inform themselves as to the conduct of those who aspired to baptism. From all who knew Tekakwitha, even from those who had ill-treated her or who might be most inclined to slander her, he heard nothing to her discredit. The day of her baptism was accordingly set for the Easter of 1676, nearly a year after her request to become a Christian.

Her aunts readily gave their consent. Her uncle had experienced her determination in matters of moment to her. Whether this moved him to unaccustomed leniency, or whether he feared that Tekakwitha might follow Ennita, Anastasia, and the other Christians to Canada, no one knew. At any rate he made no effort to prevent her baptism.

On Easter morning, April 18, St. Peter's was resplendent. The Indians had been lavish with their gifts. Bearskin rugs covered the floor, rich furs of elk and beaver, bright blankets and wampum belts, beads and embroidery hung over walls and rafters. The entrance was a bower of green leading as it were to a garden, where the altar stood laden with blooming branches and the wild flowers that grow in ravines.

The Indian girls, vivid spots of color, crowded expectantly in front of the chapel. Some of them carried their brothers and sisters in cradle boards fastened to their backs. Tekakwitha was coming. Quietly she left the lodge and walked between two companions who were also to be baptized. Men and women, boys and girls of every age, warriors, hunters, jugglers stood along the way. Oblivious of all, with downcast eyes she walked in the Easter sunlight through an avenue of budding trees that the Blackrobes had planted. The birds were building their nests in them and filling the air with the rapture of song.

The priest with his Mohawk acolytes met the three at the

door. For the first time she was called by her Christian name:

"Kateri, what do you ask of the Church of God?"

"Faith." She knew the answer well. It had burned in her heart for many a day.

"To what does Faith lead?" the priest continued.

"To Life Everlasting." How simple it was, this meeting of Time and Eternity!

When Kateri turned from the font, the blessed water still damp upon her head and a lighted candle in her hand, the earth was filled with music. The neighboring forest was alive with song; in the chapel the choir of boys and girls burst forth into the joy of Easter hymns, and in the heart of Kateri a new canticle trembled out of the silence, the primal song of the soul on the morning of a life that was new.

CHAPTER 20 At first Kateri was left unmolested in the practice of her Faith. The family did not comment when she returned to the chapel on Easter afternoon for the chanting of the rosary in alternate choirs. She had fallen in love with the Mother of the Christ Child when, as a timid stranger she had first looked upon her face. Now she knew who the Lady was and could speak to her. Now she had the sense of belonging. She would never be lonely again, and her homesick love for her mother, Kahenta, grew into this larger love for the Mother of Christ.

It was part of the nature of Kateri, that once she was sure of a duty, she walked toward it without hesitation. Her life had a new purpose and with undeviating speed she moved toward it at every moment of the day. Her course had suddenly veered from negative to positive. Hitherto she was constantly turning away from something, from the vices of her people, their cruelties, obscenities, their drunkenness. Now, with an intensity of motivation she could turn toward something, toward the Christian manner of life, toward the immortal reaches that Faith opened to her, toward an all-absorbing Love, which she grasped with all the freshness and force of the primitive at its best. The weariness of a long civilization was not in her blood. Her sense of inferiority had made her ready for humility, and from a modesty that was natural, to a purity that was supernatural, was an easy transition. The flood tide of divine Love surged into the empty places of her being, transforming physical disfigurement into "the beauty of the King's daughter" that is from within.

This gives reason to the rapidity of her flight toward holiness, and her virtues compelled the admiration even of those least inclined to imitate them. The speed of her progress, however, does not imply a way of ease. Gandawagué was still predominantly pagan, and Kateri's care for modesty of dress and behavior was a constant reproach to the lax morals prevalent in the village. From time to time attempts were made to lead her astray; they but drove her into deeper retirement, or quickened her steps to St. Peter's Chapel.

At home too, the murmuring was beginning. "What do you mean?" scolded Karitha one Sunday morning when Kateri returned from Mass. "You should be out in the field. You are at least an hour late."

"But it is Sunday, Mother. I cannot work in the field today."

"A fine excuse for your laziness," Karitha scoffed.

"I shall work harder and longer tomorrow, as I did yesterday," Kateri answered soothingly.

"That does not make up for today. She who will not work dare not eat," Karitha threatened as she took up her basket to go to the maize field. Kateri made no move to follow her.

"All right, starve if you want to, you stubborn girl!" Karitha screamed as she hurried out of the cabin.

Kateri accepted this change of attitude with her customary calm, almost as if she had expected it. It was but the first mutterings of a storm that was soon to break in all its fury. She did not neglect her household duties. She was ready as ever to help others whenever she could; but nothing that she did could please her family. When she spent her free time in prayer they found fault and Karitha made good her threat as to food. On Sundays and holydays no morsel was left in the cabin for Kateri. This did not in the least change her manner toward her relatives. She remained affable as ever; but her lips, though always ready to smile, had an added line of firmness about them. When the family saw that they gained nothing by this treatment they resorted to more violent measures.

This manifested itself on an afternoon in 1677 when, on her way to church, Kateri noticed a small, dark object flying across her head. At first she could not distinguish what it was. Then she heard something, evidently hurled with force, whistle past her ears. No one was in sight. Then she felt stones beating against her back, coming from some hiding place. It was probably the boys playing a prank; for she had always been on friendly terms with the children of the village. She did not so much as turn her head; but went quietly on her way.

The next day, however, while bent upon the same errand, the figure of a man reeled across her path. She tried to move out of his way quickly; but he shook his fist in her face, made drunken grimaces, and staggered after her. She outstripped him and arrived at the chapel, panting and exhausted. She began to see that here was a planned persecution and her nerves turned to steel to meet it. On the next occasion more men appeared, either drunk or pretending to be. They pursued her, even threatened her life; but her aspect remained fearless. She ignored them and continued on her way as though in perfect peace. At home she did not mention these occurrences; but Arosen nagged, Karitha watched her narrowly, and Iowerano had nothing friendly to say. Their plans were not as effective as they had hoped.

In the months that followed, Kateri suffered much from the taunts of drunkards, the mockeries of sorcerers and of all the enemies of "The Prayer" as they termed the teaching of the Blackrobes. The children came out into the open now and frequently followed her to church with showers of stones. They pointed their fingers at her and as a term of derision called her "The Christian" in a way that one would speak to a dog. So long did this epithet continue to be used that Kateri's real name was forgotten and she came to be generally known as "The Christian" and there were some who called her sorceress.

Throughout these attacks she showed extraordinary firmness against all ridicule or contempt. She was even happy to have lost her name for the sake of Christ and missed no opportunity of telling her antagonists that she would rather die than renounce her Faith. She was put to this test one day when alone in the cabin. Without warning a young brave rushed in upon her with eyes ablaze and a face distorted with fury. She did not recognize him; but suspected that he might be one of the ignored suitors that her aunts had provided. His tomahawk was lifted to strike, while he leveled a volley of threats at her. Without a tremor she bowed her head and stood facing him, immovable as a rock, and the silence that an Indian understands was between them. Slowly, slowly, the ferocity died in his eyes. Amazement crept into them, then awe until he stared spellbound. Her courage unnerved him and his own gave way to fear. The tomahawk dropped to his side and he slunk away. As soon as he was out of her sight he fled as though an army were pursuing him.

The master stroke had failed. It was plain to Kateri's family now, that nothing that they could contrive would intimidate her, and a period of peace followed. She was constantly exposed, however, to their reproaches that she had no affection for them and that she hated the Mohawks because of her Algonquin mother. But this unpleasantness was as nothing compared to the new trial that awaited her, the most cruel of all, and one which finally estranged her from her home and her relatives.

This happened during the spring hunting season in 1677 when Kateri went with her people in the direction of the Dutch settlement at Schenectady. Karitha's growing aversion had turned to a genuine dislike for her niece whose virtuous conduct irritated her. It had often annoyed her that Iowerano in his own way had liked the girl and sometimes taken her part. Like a lynx she watched Kateri's every word and action during the hunt in order to find some fault. Among the Indians it is customary to call an uncle by the name of father, and to treat him as such. It happened one day that Kateri in speaking of her uncle inadvertently called him by his name instead of saying "Father" or "My Father." Karitha noticed the slip at once and in her prejudiced state of mind accused Kateri of an unlawful affection for Iowerano, maintaining that she had sinned.

From this moment on, life became unbearable for the girl. Her aunt had stricken her at the most sensitive point, her purity, and Karitha displayed her suspicions in all their inhumanity. Upon their return to the village, obsessed by her evil project she went at once to Father de Lamberville and told him the hideous invention.

"So Kateri," she concluded, "whom you esteem as so virtuous is notwithstanding a hypocrite who is deceiving you."

"You are saying a terrible thing of a good Christian. What

proof have you of such an accusation?" the priest asked.

When Karitha gave her feeble reason Father de Lamberville's manner changed. "Woman," he said severely, "you have a slanderous tongue. What right have you to injure an innocent girl? You must make good the harm that you have done."

Karitha hung her head in shame and went away as quickly as she had come.

Father de Lamberville turned into the chapel. He thought long about Kateri's growing problems, and prayed over them. From the first he had felt that hers was a gifted spirit. In a wild new country, among a primitive people he had found a soul that in its purity would be rare even among Christian nations. Here in the Mohawk Valley it was a miracle when a Christian persevered. Many had become lax almost immediately after baptism and sometimes were worse than before because they were unable to stand the criticism or ridicule of their pagan relatives and friends. This was a common failing among them. Kateri, on the contrary, had not only retained the fullness of her first fervor, but her virtues were so outstanding that pagans as well as Christians noticed it.

For the Christians in general the missionary had prohibited attendance at dream feasts, dances, or other gatherings that would endanger the virtue of purity. Since Kateri had avoided these things before her baptism he gave her additional direction as to a rule of life and she had obeyed with such enthusiasm that he regretted not being able to send her to Canada. He had suggested this upon hearing of the jeers of drunkards and sorcerers, the attacks from children, the persecution at home that she was made to undergo. But Kateri felt it impossible to escape from Iowerano, who would never consent to her departure.

Father de Lamberville deplored this the more since Karitha's visit, the effects of which he was unable to shake off. He
trusted Kateri; for he had watched her conduct closely and
knew the quality of her perseverance. Nevertheless he continued to feel disturbed at what her aunt had told him. He
had instructed Kateri with great care. Could he have omitted
something? Was there some detail that she did not fully
understand? He must speak to her. Until then he would not
be satisfied.

After the evening rosary he called her and began by instructing her on sin, and the pains of hell with which God
punished it. Then he questioned her. Firmly, without hesitation she replied:

"No, Father, I have never committed this sin, not on the
occasion when my aunt accused me, nor at any other time.
I am not afraid of going to hell for this; but I am afraid of
not being brave enough to let them kill me rather than to
work in the fields on Sunday."

"But, Kateri — " the priest's voice was gentle — "did you
not often go all day without eating, when your people hid the
food in order to force you to go to the field and work?"

"Yes, Father," she admitted. "They say that Christianity
is making me lazy and worthless."

The priest shook his head. "You must leave as soon as
possible," he said with decision. "Here the struggle for peace
is too deadly."

"But my uncle, Father! I'm afraid it will never, never
happen."

He led the way back to the chapel that she might offer all
her crosses to Jesus in the Blessed Sacrament, which she did
with her whole heart. He saw that in a moment she was lost
in prayer; for to her prayer was not a duty, but a love. As

he returned to his cabin Father de Lamberville could not help contrasting Kateri's high courage with the cowardice of many other converts who, being the only Christians in their respective cabins, kept the fact well hidden from those with whom they lived.

"She is made of fine steel," he commented to himself, "pliable, but unbreakable."

To him it was becoming clear that she was not acting from a merely natural goodness. He felt convinced that God, as He so frequently does, was directing her fine human qualities, her sheltering handicaps, to new purposes and building a tremendous supernatural destiny upon them. She was not born a saint. She was a superb woman out of whom, so Father de Lamberville hoped, God was fashioning a saint.

CHAPTER 21   Ever since her latest trial Kateri had lost all attachment to her home. She would have no regrets at leaving it forever, and her longing to join the Christians in Canada grew strong. The Mission of St. Francis Xavier had moved from Laprairie to Sault St. Louis, the rapids from which the settlement derived its Indian name of Caughnawaga. The Christians from the Sault came and went frequently and at every visit Kateri was inspired with new hope. So far no one had offered to take her and she knew of no one with whom she would have cared to go.

As to her life in the long house, all hope of peace had gone forever. The chief was sullen and sat brooding about his half-emptied village. The departure of Kryn was still like a bitter taste in his mouth. He treated Kateri brusquely, was displeased with everything that she did, and yet continued to refuse his consent to her leaving. The aunts nagged or lapsed into moody silence. Tekakwitha saw no outlook other than to strengthen her forces of endurance and be patient.

At Sault St. Louis or Caughnawaga, both Anastasia and her sister Ennita, who occupied the same cabin, were thinking anxious thoughts of Kateri and longing to have her share their security. Fervor was at a high point at this mission of St. Francis Xavier which had become not only a refuge for Christian Indians but a nurturing place for heroic souls.

Numerous stories of thrilling spiritual adventure belong to
this early century in the long history of the mission. One of
the great leaders in the life at Caughnawaga was a certain
Louis Garonhiague, an Oneida chief, whose name translated
means Hot Powder or Hot Ashes, Poudre Chaude as the
French called him, who had arrived at the mission by a
circuitous path.

As his name indicates, he had a stormy temperament, and
he left Oneida in fury after quarreling with a neighbor.
Filled with resentment he went on the hunt. During that
time the news that his brother had been killed added more
fuel to his violent temper. With his customary impetuosity
he leaped to the conclusion that the French were responsible,
and with all speed he rushed toward Montreal to avenge his
brother. On the way he discovered that someone else, not
the French, was guilty of the murder. He was near the
mission of the Sault where he decided to stop and plan his
next step. The Indians of the village liked him at once and
the place had a calming effect upon him. In trying to solve
his problem he realized that if he returned home he would
most certainly avenge his brother's death. This would force
his whole tribe into war; for he knew that out of loyalty to
him they would join in his vengeance. He therefore decided
to remain at the mission. His wife, Marie Garhi, who was
strongly inclined to Christianity, and as gentle as he was
turbulent, came with their children to make a home for him.
Not long after their arrival he requested instruction and
with all his family was baptized.

He entered upon his new life with all the fire that was
a part of him. The story of the mission includes many evidences of his apostolic zeal. On one occasion while hunting
he came upon a band of half-drunk Oneidas sitting around

a cask of liquor sold to them by a Frenchman who refilled it whenever it was empty. The Oneidas invited him to join them. He drank a little, then resorted to a trick in order to avoid offending God and to prevent the others from falling more deeply into sin. To try to stop them would be of no avail, so he pretended to be drunk and while singing and dancing kicked over the cask and spilled the liquor. They laughed uproariously and made fun of his awkwardness until night was upon them, then forgot all about drinking, and fell soundly asleep.

Many of the Oneidas came to visit Hot Powder at the mission and ended by becoming Christians. His gift of leadership was so evident that he was soon chosen as fourth chieftain of Caughnawaga. With a completeness of dedication his fiery nature turned itself to works of zeal. Not only did he keep the liquor traffic out of the settlement, but by preaching and teaching, and by his good example he attracted many to Christianity.

This was the man destined to go to the rescue of Kateri. Iowerano could never have intimidated Hot Powder, and while the girl was longing with diminishing hope to leave that desert of the spirit in which she lived, Hot Powder with Ennita's husband and a Huron from Lorette set out for the Valley of the Mohawks. Upon arrival they went directly to St. Peter's Chapel to begin their visit with prayer. Father de Lamberville received them warmly, the elders of the village paid their respects to the Oneida chief, and many of the Mohawks, drawn by curiosity, came to see them. When Hot Powder saw the crowd gathering about him, he spoke to them with all his native eloquence, telling them of the Christian Faith and what it meant to him. One after another the elders left, and after a while Hot Powder found himself almost alone; but the discourtesy did not stop him. Not far away a girl in a long blue shawl was listening with spellbound ears.

As soon as she found Father de Lamberville alone she ran to him: "Father! I must go away, even if it costs me my life."

"We shall see, Kateri. I think the time has come."

Father de Lamberville discussed the matter with Hot Powder and the plans were soon completed. That Chief Iowerano was away was most favorable to the contemplated escape. Hot Powder would go to the Oneidas and preach the Faith among the other Iroquois nations and Kateri could take his place in the canoe which he had concealed near the shore of Lake George. But they must act at once, lose no time, and leave under cover of darkness. His two companions, the Mohawk Onas and Jacques the Huron, would guide her safely to Canada. Onas could find a canoe here in the village, they could paddle a short distance down the river, then take to the woods for greater safety.

Kateri did not sleep that night. In addition to the excitement of her intended flight she was loath, as it were, even for a moment to lose the awareness of her approaching release. Every little while she felt for the letter that lay on the mat beside her. Father de Lamberville was placing her under the care of Father Cholenec at the Sault. She would have been stricken with embarrassment had she known the contents.

"Kateri Tekakwitha is going to live at the Sault," the priest wrote. "Will you kindly undertake to direct her? You will soon know what a treasure we have sent you. Guard it well! May it profit in your hands, for the glory of God, and the salvation of a soul that is certainly very dear to Him."

Kateri realized during that exuberant night, that she was

at a great dividing point in her life. She was too honest to play with any sentimental thoughts about the home that she was leaving, although she did love the land that she knew. She loved the Valley of the Mohawks, the gentle hills with the speeding river between, the sound of unleashed waters in spring, the glory of the woods in autumn. These were the little loves that had called to her in childhood and companioned the solitude of her growing years. But the great Love toward which, half blindly, she had groped her way, had come at last. Its tremendous power had absorbed all lesser attachments and given them a meaning and a place. This Love she would follow over any great divide, the Indian in her keyed to the hunt, fearless of the wild and lonely places.

Kateri did not formulate these things to herself during that wakeful night; but they were there, and strong within her. And over all like a cool and quiet hand, lay the parting blessing of the Blackrobe, keeping her calm and at peace, despite the uncertain journey that lay ahead, the danger of pursuit, the mystery of the coming years. Noiselessly she slipped out of the long house and into the darkness of the hour before the dawn. Two deeper shadows emerged from the shadowed square and without a word led the way out of the sleeping village down to the riverbank.

After the worn trail along the eastern bank of the Hudson had turned northeast and they had passed safely through the valley into the mountain country surrounding the Lake of the Blessed Sacrament, which the English named Lake George, Kateri paused and looked up to the summits about her. A hymn of gratitude surged through her heart and the wings of her spirit opened wide to this new freedom. In the moment when her infuriated uncle within a few steps of her suddenly turned and gave up the chase, she had her first experience of the nearness of the Divine Providence and all fear of tomorrow and then tomorrow vanished like vapor.

They found the canoe that Hot Powder had left in the shrubs, and paddled up the western shore of Lake George, where the water was smoothest. Light of heart, they sang their Iroquois hymns while in the distant Mohawk Valley the old chief sat brooding and disconsolate beside the fire. Scarcely a ripple stirred the water glowing in the westward slant of the sun. While they were passing Ticonderoga, Onas lingered for a moment.

"The little people are not angry today," he said with a smile of amusement, recalling the pagan custom of paying tribute to the little people under the water when leaving the so-called tail of the lake. These sprites were believed to prepare the arrow flints with which that part of the shore was strewn. To gain their good will the pagans threw tobacco into the lake, for when it was rough they thought the little people angry. But the thoughts of the three Christian Indians went into other channels. For them the presence of Jogues was walking over the waters that he had named, and Kateri was retracing the way that her mother had come. Kahenta had sown in tears, walking the tortuous path of a captive. Kateri reaped in the joy of an escape. With every mile this joy increased as they skimmed the surface of Lake Champlain lying like a sapphire in the October sunshine, as they drew nearer and nearer to the place of peace, the Praying Castle on the St. Lawrence.

During the swift journey Tekakwitha had broken completely with the old life, and fear, like a weight, fell from her. She was twenty-one now, and in the fullness of her womanhood.

CHAPTER 22 Kateri gave a little gasp of wonder at sight of the St. Lawrence and the tall maples of the Canadian forest bursting into light and flame. An aging woman was standing on the shore line waiting. She opened her arms with a cry of joy.

"Anastasia!" And Kateri was folded in an embrace that she knew. Ennita came running from her cabin. They had been taking turns watching for the travelers. When Kateri found herself in the place prepared for her in the cabin where Onas and Ennita lived and where Anastasia was mistress, she felt that she had come home. There was no barrier now in her relations with Anastasia. She who had known Kahenta and seen her die would mother Kahenta's child, teach her, and help her in her growing. It was she who took her to the bark chapel and presented her to the Blackrobes, one of whom was just coming out of the church as they approached.

"Welcome, little Tekakwitha," a cheery voice called, and she recognized the first Blackrobe that she had ever seen, Father Frémin, one of the three guests at her uncle's lodge, long ago when she was a child. She had not grown tall and to him she seemed the same little girl that he remembered carrying her jug from the spring, gathering wood in the forest, coming to him timidly with the bowl of sagamite. The smile of the child had not gone from her gentle eyes, nor had they lost their look of innocence; but something that came with her womanhood had been added. "One might call it sinlessness," the priest said to himself, knowing as he did the evils to which she had been exposed. He noticed also that her native amiability, far from turning into weakness had grown into strength. Father Pierron's extraordinary comment came to his mind: "She has the manners of a well brought up French child." She had them still; but they had matured into the warmth of human kindness, and Father Frémin suspected that they included also the more profound charm of Christian charity.

Kateri handed him the letter that Father de Lamberville had given her. "Here comes Father Cholenec now. He will have charge of you. It is he who instructs the converts, prepares them for baptism and their First Holy Communion."

Kateri looked trustingly up into the strong, smiling face of Father Cholenec. He read the letter and the two priests exchanged significant glances.

"Father Chauchetière!" Father Frémin called to another Blackrobe coming out of the cabin, "you must meet my little friend, Kateri. We have known one another a long time. She took good care of us when we were guests at her uncle's long house when she was still a very little pagan girl. We must be good to her now and make her feel at home here in Caughnawaga."

"I hope you will be happy with us, my child," said Father Chauchetière gently, fixing his bright, enthusiastic eyes upon her. Anastasia beamed.

"And now you must see our chapel," said Father Frémin, leading the way. "It is very small, too small for our congregation. Next spring we must build a new one. We already have three bells and we shall soon have a fourth to complete the harmony," Father Frémin explained. Kateri was wordless with wonderment, most of all at the feeling within her. For the first time since the misty morning of life, she had the sense of home. Now she knew that she had been a stranger in a strange land even as Kahenta her mother had been.

Anastasia took her through the byways of the village and she was welcomed by many a familiar voice that she had known in the Mohawk Valley. All were eager for news of their former homes and of the people left behind; but not one would have been willing to return. She barely recognized the wife of Kryn, her aspect was so cheerful. Breathlessly everyone listened to the story of her escape, the pursuit by her uncle, her all but miraculous deliverance, which Anastasia told and retold.

Caughnawaga or Sault St. Louis, often simply called the Sault, which lay on the south bank of the St. Lawrence, several miles west of Montreal, numbered one hundred twenty to one hundred fifty families with at least two in each cabin. There were sixty cabins in all. Since the village lay high it commanded a far-reaching view over the river which at that point was churned by the roaring rapids and assumed the proportions of a lake.

Kateri stirred in her sleep and wondered where she was. A thin stream of sound filtered through the darkness. It was the four o'clock bell on her first morning at Caughnawaga; for the Blackrobes timed their rising hour with that of their brethren in France. Many of the more devout among the Indians, not to be outdone by the missionaries, responded with alacrity to the summons, hurrying quietly through the streets to adore the Blessed Sacrament, in preparation for the first Mass of the day, which in summer was at five o'clock, and during the winter at a quarter to seven. The second Mass followed immediately. All the people of the village, without a single exception, attended, and they prayed aloud together. The third Mass was for the children, who also prayed aloud, and this was followed by a short instruction on the Catechism given by Father Chauchetière.

Frequently during the day the Indians visited the chapel on their way to and from the fields. The mission was afire with its first fervor and its Christians were animated by the spirit of the primitive Church. We have Father Cholenec's written word for it that God Himself was outspokenly the first and most vital concern of these Indians. Everybody, he says, was living a life of holiness, the youngest as well as the oldest, vying with one another, and making nearly all the lodges into schools of virtue and holiness.

Kateri found herself in a different world, with her life facing the challenge of conforming itself to a new pattern, and her ardent spirit was on fire with the thrill and the beauty of it. She enjoyed meeting the new converts, many of whom were old friends, and she marveled at the change in their manner of life in so short a time after they had left the country of the Iroquois. With her well-ordered inner faculties, her generous heart, and all the forces of her character grown strong amid the pressures of her life among the pagans, she seized the more avidly upon every opportunity to learn what was good and to translate her knowledge into action. She did this with the same passion for perfection with which she wove her wampum and fashioned her bowls out of bark, choosing from among the good things those that she recognized as the best, with the result that within a few weeks she made such progress that even among the girls and women of this striving mission, she distinguished herself in holiness of life.

It often happened that her keen intuitions and the direct line along which she moved brought her to objectives to which she did not know the separate steps. Happily Anastasia had a rare gift for instructing and she lavished the fullness of her solicitude upon her new charge. Whether in cabin, field, or forest, the two were seldom separated. At first Anastasia tutored Kateri in the ordinary exercises of the mission for feasts and working days, and they discussed the lives of the saints and the problems of sin and penance, heaven and hell. More and more, even in this Christian environment, Kateri loved solitude and sought only those acquaintances who could lead her to perfection.

"And what did you do, my Kateri, after I left the Mohawk Valley?" Anastasia asked one day.

"The usual things, Anastasia, the work of a squaw," Kateri answered smiling. Then a light shot into her eyes. "But Easter and baptism! It was heaven, Anastasia." She described it in detail; but omitted any allusion to the months of persecution that followed.

"You look the same, Kateri, as when I saw you last," the woman continued, "with the beads around your neck and in your hair. Do you like them very much?"

Kateri looked surprised. "They are pretty," she said, "but they mean nothing to me. I have always used them according to the customs of our people. I am foolish, Anastasia, and ignorant. You must have much patience with me."

Anastasia proceeded with her questioning: "Tell me, Kateri, do you love the Blessed Virgin?"

The response in the girl's face would have been sufficient to satisfy the most exacting of mentors; but Anastasia had not finished.

"Would you be willing," she continued, "to give up these vanities in imitation of the Blessed Virgin?"

"Why certainly," Kateri replied without hesitation. She took them off at once and never wore them again.

There was something more on Anastasia's mind. She alluded to it one day while they were sitting by the fire, Anastasia mending a pair of moccasins, Kateri braiding rushes into a mat. Anastasia surveyed the moccasin in her hand critically. Should she speak of the matter now? she pondered, trying to gain a little time.

"Wouldn't you like to marry, Kateri?" she asked in a casual tone. "You are of marriageable age now and you need no longer fear the pagan braves."

The rushes swished ever so slightly in Kateri's hands; but she looked up and smiled. "No, dear Anastasia; I have no such desire."

The woman did not press her further and quickly changed the subject. With the thoroughness characteristic of her, and mindful always of her responsibility as teacher and second mother, she proceeded to speak of slander, saying that it was a recurring fault especially among the squaws, one into which it was easy even for a good Christian to fall. Kateri's soft, intelligent eyes opened wide as she asked:

"What is slander, Anastasia?"

CHAPTER **23** Kateri soon found that
her new home had been rightly named the Praying Castle
on the St. Lawrence. In its atmosphere of recollection her
spirit expanded to its fullest functioning. Her increasing love
of solitude did not prevent her from feeling the solidarity of
the community and its sustaining power. The strength of the
whole went into each member of a group living in such
unison of purpose that by common consent as it were, every
detail of life was ordered toward a single goal.

The people of the Sault were God-conscious, and if there
was emulation among them, it was in the practice of virtue.
This inevitably engendered a spirit of charity and sometimes
the hospitality of brotherhood went so far that in order to
help a newcomer the settlers willingly gave over their own
well-prepared fields and broke new ground for themselves.
The mission had already built a tradition. The number of
honored names was increasing and Kateri soon found that
her name of Katharine was held in great veneration because
of a Katharine Ganneaktewa, whom they regarded as a saint
and to whom, next to Father Raffeix, the original settlement
at Laprairie owed its beginnings. This extraordinary woman
who had been of inestimable help to the Blackrobes even
while still a pagan, was among the first chosen by Father
Pierron when he established the Congregation of the Holy

Family. That long-lived, powerful influence which in its early days inspired the Indians to mold their lives upon those of the Holy Family, continues to exist in the Caughnawaga of today.

In these propitious surroundings Kateri rose steadily into higher spiritual altitudes. Like all the other driving forces within her, the desire for solitude had developed into something different from the inclination of her pagan days partly conditioned perhaps by environment and her physical handicaps. This new solitude was a creative thing, the result of her oneness of purpose and a wholeness in the manner of attaining it. Never had she spent her strength upon unworthy affections; therefore when she found God, she loved Him with a heart that was whole. As a consequence she spared no effort in seeking all possible ways of pleasing Him and in avoiding the slightest thing that might impede her union with Him. These simple facts, basic to all sanctity, are the key to the life of Kateri. Through the medium of her personality and its setting they assumed an aspect, an individual quality of light, that was new upon the earth. Hers was the nature of a child of the forest, a combination of the fierce-willed Mohawk and the gentler Algonquin, directed by the quiet of a strong interior life, into a mode of being that was new, and that turned with full acquiescence to the compelling light that Faith shed upon it.

Father Cholenec sensed this when he said to Father Frémin: "I believe that the longer period of probation for First Holy Communion, that we usually demand among the Iroquois, should be shortened for Kateri Tekakwitha."

"You are right, Father," the Superior replied, "not only is her conduct irreproachable; but in her devotion and the enthusiasm with which she enters into the life of the mission, she is already outstripping our other Christians."

Father Chauchetière's eyes glowed as he listened, then he added: "Even Anastasia who watches her so carefully has said that she lives constantly in the presence of God."

"I shall tell her that she may receive our Lord on Christmas day," said Father Cholenec. "She will have been here little more than two months; but she is too well disposed to be deprived of this grace."

For Kateri this first Christmas in Canada was the fulfillment of the story of Bethlehem that Father Boniface had told in the Mohawk Valley while she, a pagan, was looking in rapture at the Christmas crib. This was the Christ Child alive, and He had come into her heart! We cannot pry into the soul of Kateri, enfolded in the mystery, the wonderment, the reality of that first meeting. We cannot capture those moments of interchange, but in the words of Father Cholenec: "All that we can say is that from that day forward she appeared different to us, because she remained so full of God and of love for Him." And this same biographer who was also Kateri's spiritual guide gives the assurance that in the frequent Communions that followed, her first fervor did not abate. This was so evident to all in the village that at a time of general Communion the most devout of the women tried to find a place near her, maintaining that the mere sight of her inspired them and provided an excellent preparation for receiving the Sacrament.

CHAPTER 24 Christmas of 1677 had passed. The river was locked in ice and January snows lay heavy on the trees and over the countryside. The stir of departure, as group after group set out for the winter hunt, had subsided. Except for the sick and disabled, the cabins were empty. A few old squaws sat about the fire, and braves for whom the hunting days were over puffed silently at their pipes. The Blackrobes had a respite and spent the quiet days in prayer and study. From Caughnawaga the hunting parties went to the woods that extended northward from the Adirondacks. There they erected a camp of temporary lodges made of bark and closely woven boughs. They always carried many furs and skins with them, both to wear and to hang over openings and cracks in their quickly constructed cabins.

The hunting season was the time of hard work for the men. They left in the morning, tracked animals all day long, and did not return until evening. The women went to gather the game that the men had killed, prepared it for food, and dressed the skins. Much time however remained for the making of collars and moccasins, for their beading and embroidery over which they laughed and chatted for hours.

The hunters of the Praying Castle were Indians still and loved the life of the forest, the chase for game, the track of the deer on the frozen snow, the beaver surprised in his burrow. The women too were eager for the change and what seemed to them the easy life of the woods, with its abundant food, its lesser household tasks. They were comfortable, wrapped in their furs and blankets, sitting about the fires in their bark shelters.

Kateri had no desire for the feasting and felt no need for diversion. On the contrary, she would miss the joy of daily Masses, Benedictions, the divine human Presence in the Tabernacle. She went only to satisfy Ennita and Onas; besides, Anastasia too was with them. She remembered the ribald season in the Mohawk Valley and shuddered. Here at least the hunt would be a totally different thing. The catechists were with them, morning and evening prayers were said in common, and the spirit of the mission prevailed.

Although Kateri was not in her element she was no passive participant in the life of the hunting camp. The love of her First Communion was still burning like a white light within her. Driven by this recent experience she molded life in the forest into something new, an example forever of virtue as a sturdy thing and not a matter of time or place. She could love God whether in the woods or in the village. She could pray walking through the snow as well as on her knees in the chapel, and in that carefree environment she regulated her life according to a well-planned pattern.

Resourceful as always, since she had no chapel she made a cross from a tree in a snowbound solitude to which she could withdraw as to a little island of peace and prayer. It lay on the bank of a stream, a little apart from a path trodden into the snow by the women when they carried their jugs to an opening in the ice where the water flowed freely. In all the white country around her it was the one spot where the branches, burdened with snow, leaned down to form a natural shelter, and for her a shrine.

Before dawn, while the crowded camp was still asleep and the trees cracked with cold, Kateri was awake and praying. Later, after morning prayers said in common, while the men were eating and the women bustling about, she slipped unnoticed down to the stream. It was the hour of Mass in the village and in the congealing cold she knelt in rapt participation, following the Mass in spirit from beginning to end. As she later confided to a companion, she sent her Guardian Angel to assist at the Holy Sacrifice in her stead and begged him to return to her with its graces.

Every morning after the men had left, approximately at nine o'clock, she returned to the women and with her usual gaiety did whatever was asked of her, whether cooking the soup, cutting wood, or going with the others to collect the meat of the animals killed by the hunters. She liked especially, when gathering fuel to go farther into the forest alone to be away from the ceaseless chatter of the women. During most of the day, however, she sat with the women around the roaring fires, embroidering, beading, making collars of elk or deerskin and belts of wampum. Here Kateri was of great service; for not one of the squaws had fingers as skillful as hers. Willingly always, she dropped her own work to help the others, to plan their designs, to show them stitches or new combinations of color. They watched her eagerly, especially when she shaped the wood into chests with an art that was quite her own.

But their tongues were busier than hers and many a time the bone needles paused or the porcupine quills stopped in mid-air while spicy bits of gossip slipped into the conversation. Then Kateri, on the alert, would say: "Anastasia told me such a beautiful story. Would you like to hear it?"

"Tell, tell, Kateri," they responded with eager voices, not

suspecting that she was but adroitly changing the conversation. They fell into the little ruse easily and one after another of them had a story to relate, something heard from the Blackrobes, perhaps tales and legends from France that, from the eloquence of the Indian, gained many a picturesque detail in the telling and made them forget all about the petty faults of their neighbors.

At another time when frivolity or gossip ran high, a slight lull would enable Kateri to turn to the girl beside her and say:

"Onetoia, you have a lovely voice. Won't you sing for us?" And the girl, who sang in the choir at home, would begin a hymn which the others quickly took up. The Iroquois have pleasing voices and a natural gift for music. They sang with enthusiasm, and the hymns of the Church, varied with their own native songs, rang out through the winter silence of the woods.

Anastasia, spiritually seasoned as she was, marveled at her pupil. She noticed that when occasion required it, Kateri was capable of assuming a tactful leadership; but most of all she saw her put into practice every lesson that she had learned, charging every moment with the import of eternity and making it burn with the love that was giving her sordid life its fullness of meaning. There was much too that Anastasia did not know. She did not suspect that long after the general night prayers were over, when the others were sound asleep on their mats, Kateri was still on her knees. She was totally unaware of the fact that her own instructions on sin, the punishment of hell, the penances of the saints, had fallen upon such responsive soil that Kateri, in the seclusion of her snowbound oratory, often scourged herself when it was too cold to pray.

The girl's humility, first of all, made her regard herself as a sinner who needed penance. Furthermore she was acutely aware of the sins of her pagan people, and with the tribal sense that belongs to the Mohawk she felt herself urged to make reparation for their guilt. In this also she was resourceful, eluding observation and finding hidden ways to satisfy her desire for penance. Amid an abundance of meat she would fast unnoticed by leaving the cabin to gather wood before the sagamite was ready, and not returning until evening. Or, she would often mix ashes into her food when obliged to eat. All this she did with a complete disregard of fatigue or natural weakness; for she suffered cruelly from the severity of the Canadian winter and Anastasia was troubled when she saw her trembling uncontrollably in her blue shawl while other women were cozily wrapped in their beaver or marten furs.

Kateri had no husband to hunt for her. She did not wish to be a burden to others and contributed generously to the comfort of the cabin by her tireless industry and her many skills. Had she bartered her pieces of handicraft she could easily have supplied herself with furs; but she wanted no more than bare necessity required.

"This is foolish, Kateri," Anastasia would remonstrate whenever she was struck anew by the girl's aspect of poverty among the well-dressed squaws about her. "You must make up your mind to marry."

Kateri always looked up from her embroidery and smiled engagingly into Anastasia's eyes; but the older woman refused to be diverted.

"I mean it, and it is for your own sake," she continued. "You can see here in the forest, how much it means to have a hunter to provide for you. Besides, it is the proper thing to do," Anastasia concluded, tugging emphatically at her thread made of the sinews of deer. Kateri's sense of humor could not resist this opportunity.

"Dear Anastasia," she said with the sudden light of fun darting into her eyes, "if you think so well of it, why don't you marry?" An outburst of laughter came from the other squaws and the corners of Anastasia's firm mouth twitched with amusement that she could not quite conceal. She had been a widow for many years; but had a host of relatives who provided for her, young, unmarried braves any one of whom she would gladly have seen Kateri accept as a husband. Kateri however remained completely indifferent to the advantages of a good marriage and even Anastasia found this attitude hard to understand.

Despite Tekakwitha's serenity, her humor, her uncomplaining helpfulness, she did not grow to feel at home with her life in the woods, and an unpleasant occurrence toward the end of the season confirmed her resolution never again to return to the hunt. One of the men of their company, having spent the whole day chasing an elk, returned to the lodge very late. Even Kateri was asleep. The hunter was so exhausted that he threw himself down in the nearest place without even taking anything to eat or drink. When his wife awoke on the following morning, not finding him near her she looked about the cabin and saw him sound asleep near Kateri's mat. The woman, Nemahbin, knew Kateri but slightly, and being unaware of the shrine down near the brook, began to recall her comings and goings, with an ugly suspicion growing in her mind.

Later in the day, quite inadvertently, her husband Onsigongo, spoke of his canoe which needed mending before the journey home.

"One of you squaws," he said, "must help me with the canoe. Tekakwitha, you come. You are clever with the needle."

This was enough for Nemahbin. Fortunately she was a good woman and sufficiently discreet not to disclose her thoughts. She would tell no one but the Blackrobe after her return to the mission. Onsigongo was utterly unconscious of the whole affair. A Christian for twenty years, he had never given his wife the least trouble, nor would he ever do so. Nevertheless for Kateri a cross was in the making that was to cause her the greatest agony of all her suffering life.

The Blackrobe was troubled. He knew Kateri well, her innocent life, her horror at the slightest sin. And yet, Nemahbin was one of the most virtuous women of the mission. She had told him the whole story and it would seem that the accused could not be altogether free from guilt. He must speak to Kateri. He was so sure of her sincerity that he decided to listen to her explanation and to believe it.

On the following day he saw her in the chapel and called her. She came, looking up at him with her open, trusting glance, the same as always. There was not a flicker of suspicion, not a shadow of shame in her eyes.

"My child," he began, "I have an important question to ask you." She listened quietly while he told her of the accusation brought against her.

"Tell me, is it true, my child?" — "No, Father; it is not true." Her expression did not change. She showed no emotion. She maintained the dignity of one who knew herself to be absolutely innocent. The priest, deeply moved at her peace of soul in face of so humiliating an accusation to which she would naturally be most sensitive, decided in her favor.

Nemahbin, however, was not convinced, and a few other squaws who had learned of the matter, shared her view. Even Anastasia spoke to Kateri about remedying the evil if there was any, or of preventing it. The priest believed her now;

but she knew by his questioning and by his exhortation at the beginning of their conversation, that there had been some uncertainty in his mind. The hurt was acute. The calumny of her aunt, which no one had believed, was as nothing in comparison. The wound went deep into her spirit; but deeper still, and stronger, was her love. She had given herself, all that she had or might have had, to God. But this was a greater gift: herself dismantled, cleft, stripped of that which made her most herself, honor, reputation, her very integrity. And she gave it gladly, generously, glad to be held in contempt, glad to be regarded as a sinner. She loved enough, even for this. Therefore she made no effort to ascertain who it was that had spoken evil of her. She prayed for them all and let the matter die as though it had never been.

But God did not let it die. As usual in His dealings with human beings, He was not to be outdone in generosity. After Tekakwitha's death, in the very place where she had suffered, such marvels were to follow upon invoking her intercession, that those who had defamed her, stricken with remorse were the first to publicize her virtues. Nemahbin, inconsolable, continued for three full years to bewail her fault, imagining that God would never forgive her, until the missionary, using all his authority, was finally able to restore her peace of soul.

Kateri meantime, did not need to wait until after death, to be given consolation. She was participating to the full in the sorrow, the beauty, the joy of Holy Week and Easter, her first at the mission. It was all a part of the progressive experience of her faith translating itself into the complete surrender of which her words are the symbols: "I offer my soul to Christ the Lord in the Blessed Sacrament and my body to Christ the Lord hanging on the cross." Again, this is a key to Kateri's life and to all the details that entered into it. It is the Christian's gift to Christ, individualized in a primitive American, a daughter of the Mohawks.

On Easter, the day of her second Holy Communion, Father Cholenec gave her a wondrous surprise by admitting her into the Confraternity of the Holy Family. This was indeed a public tribute to her virtue and a sign of her complete vindication in his eyes; for this society into which only a small number were received was regarded as the summit of the spiritual life of the mission. Kateri, still very young and having spent only seven or eight months at the Sault, achieved something that had been given to others only at an advanced age and after several years of probation.

In her usual way, Tekakwitha considered herself unworthy of this honor and felt it the more incumbent upon her to work at her own perfection in order not to lower the standard of this group. With renewed severity she looked upon her shortcomings while living in the Mohawk Valley, and they became one of the principal motivations for her austerities. By chastising her body she was as she thought, but doing her duty; for Anastasia had brought home the lesson that the Iroquois Christians had more reason to perform severe penances because they had so often offended God amid the disorders of their country.

An accident happening at the time augmented this frame of mind in Kateri. She was in the forest one day cutting down a tree and it fell sooner than she expected. One of the branches hit her head with such force that it struck her unconscious and her companions thought her dead. She revived with a prayer of thanksgiving and came to the conclusion that God in His mercy had preserved her so that she might do penance for her sins.

CHAPTER 25 The snowdrops and the
earliest violets were blooming again along the banks of the
St. Lawrence, and here and there a wild narcissus was forcing
its way up through the soil. Kateri stood for a moment looking out over the river, breathing deeply the softening air of
spring, her first in this northern country. She welcomed the
hint of newborn life and the roar of the rapids after the
frozen stillness. The winter held no pleasant memories. It
had ended with a crash as of doom when the ice in broken
pillars went thundering down the river. Now, from the high
point where she stood, she watched in awe the great river,
which was so much more formidable than the familiar
Mohawk.

The new wooden chapel was almost finished. It was under
roof, the floor had been laid, and the carpenters were working at the panels. As she drew nearer she saw someone else
walking around the church, looking about first on the outside
then on the inside, a robust young squaw apparently some
years older than she. According to her dress and general
appearance she belonged to the Oneida nation of the Iroquois.
They passed one another several times and Kateri was struck
by the power in the face of the squaw, her free and fearless
glance, the life in her eyes, her fine, aquiline profile. Marie
Thérèse Tegaiaguenta on her part looked at Kateri and was

immediately attracted to her, to the quiet charm of her demeanor, the sense of peace that she brought with her.

Their glances met at last and there was mutual greeting in them. The eyes of Marie Thérèse were warm, restless, searching; Kateri's shy and withdrawn, yet friendly. Something made Kateri speak despite her usual timidity.

"Where do you think will the women's places be in the new church?" she ventured.

"I believe they should be here on the gospel side," Marie Thérèse replied. The next was utterly spontaneous. It came from the unhealed wound deep down in the spirit of Kateri. She was thinking aloud.

"In reality this wooden chapel is not what God most wants of us." The words came of themselves. "He longs to live in our souls and to make them His temples."

Marie Thérèse, usually so ready with a reply, found no words; but her eyes waited eagerly.

"As for me," Kateri continued, and her voice was low and tense, "I do not deserve to enter this chapel." She did not suspect that every word struck fire in the soul of Marie Thérèse and tortured her. She could not have sensed the storms through which the Oneida had passed, her temperament of flame, the extremes of good and evil between which her life had swung. She could not know that the unpremeditated words leaping to life from her own humility and complete abjection of spirit, had redemption in them.

Then Marie Thérèse spoke: "It is I who should be saying such things, not you."

Her heart opened and she told of her desires to serve God, to remain quietly at the mission, to do penance for her sins and learn to lead a holy life. They understood one another at once, and in the shadow of the unfinished chapel a friendship was sealed that was not to end with death, for the light of eternity was upon it.

Slowly they walked as they talked, Kateri telling of her life in the Mohawk Valley, her conversion, her escape to Canada. They reached the tall cross on the edge of the river and instinctively sat down at the foot of it.

"Mine is a long and harrowing story," Marie Thérèse began. "As a young married woman I was baptized by Father Bruyas in my country of the Oneidas. My husband was not a Catholic. I was not like you, Kateri, and was much too weak to resist the temptations around me. The pagans made it extremely difficult for the Christians and tried especially to make drunkards of them, to win them away from the influence of the Blackrobes. Some of the Christians were very courageous. One of the squaws fought with her hands and nails while keeping her lips locked, to prevent some men from forcing the firewater down her throat. I was not so brave and soon fell a victim to drunkenness. I even belonged to the Society of the Dark Dance, a hideous thing that I would rather forget, and I nearly lost my Faith." Marie Thérèse shuddered as though trying to shake some horrible memory from her thoughts. She continued in a calmer tone:

"After Katharine Ganneaktena, one of the leading squaws of our country, who had been such a help to Father Bruyas, had settled at Laprairie, our family also went there to live; but even there I lapsed into my old fault.

"In the early autumn of 1675 I left with my husband and my sister's little boy to go hunting along the Ottawa River. On the way we met other Iroquois with whom we formed a party of eleven: four men, four women, and three children. Unhappily the snow fell late that year and we were unable to hunt. After our provisions were gone and we had eaten an elk that my husband had killed, we began to suffer hunger. At first we ate some small skins which we had brought to make moccasins, then we ate even the moccasins, and finally were forced like animals to eat herbs and the bark of trees.

"Then my husband became sick and two of the men, a Mohawk and a Seneca decided to go farther away to hunt, promising to return in ten days at the latest. We were full of hope; but on the tenth day the Mohawk returned alone and without any game. He told us that the Seneca had died of starvation; but a horrible fear came over us that the Mohawk had killed him and lived on his flesh while away. We felt certain of it after he admitted that he had found no game; because he seemed to be well fed and in perfect health.

"Since my husband was too ill to be of any use they tried to persuade me to let him die in order to save myself, my nephew, and the others. This of course I refused to do and I had to resist repeatedly with panic growing in my heart."

At this point a tremor shook Kateri who had not moved and was sitting with her eyes fastened upon the Oneida.

"They finally abandoned me," Marie Thérèse continued, "and I was left alone with my sick husband and the boy. Two days later my husband died, regretting that he had not let the Blackrobe baptize him. I buried him and took the road again, carrying the boy on my shoulders; he was little more than a skeleton. In a few days I came upon the Indians who had left me. They were weak and exhausted, looking for the road down the river to the French village. They stared at me with desperation in their eyes and something of a menace; for they were facing starvation and death. They had decided to kill one of their number that the rest might live.

"The first victim was an old man, so exhausted that he

could scarcely keep up with the others. They killed him and offered me some of his flesh to eat. It sickened me and I could not. This aroused their curiosity. While they were eating they began to question me:

" 'You are the only one of us who is baptized. Tell us, was it permissible to kill this man?'

" 'What does the Christian law say about it?' another interposed.

"I was speechless with fear while they continued to discuss the matter, giving reasons why the man should forfeit his right to live.

" 'He was too tired,' one of them said. 'He was unable to hunt and was of no help to us,' said another.

" 'He would have given us a great deal of trouble on the way,' said a third, and so it went on: 'We have nothing to eat. We would all die.'

"I was as one struck dumb. Had I consented to the murder they would doubtless have felt free to kill me in order to save the lives of the others. I could think of nothing but how bitterly sorry I was for having come to the hunt without going to confession.

"We moved onward toward the French settlement at Ville Marie; but lost our way in the snow and were so numb with cold that our progress was slow and we faced starvation again. I saw hungry eyes fastening themselves upon one after another of us. The widow of the Seneca paled as they fell upon her and her two children, knowing that she was useless to them. Then they turned to me and I could read the mute question in them. My heart went dead within me. My nephew and I were the other useless ones."

Marie Thérèse's horror-filled eyes looked far out over the river. She was lost in the forest again. She was facing a gruesome death once more. Kateri was motionless, her hands tightly locked.

"I can see them yet," she began with an effort, "eating, eating, a half crazed glow in their eyes. My body ached in every limb. I could scarcely drag it through the snow. Then the thought of my soul, a thousand times more miserable than my body, haunted me like an evil spirit until I wanted to sink into the snow and die; but I was afraid, more afraid than of the eyes of my hungering companions. I wanted to run and could not move.

" 'Oh! God!' I cried out with a voice that strangled in my throat, 'forgive me, a wicked woman! Only save me from this danger. I cannot walk any farther. Help me to reach the village and I'll confess my sins and do penance, much penance, Rawenniio! God!'

"That day I saw tracks in the snow and I screamed, louder than the wind:

" 'Look, look, an animal!' It could not be an elk. The tracks were smaller, lighter. The hunters, only three of them now, lifted their haggard faces and began the chase. They had not far to go. It was a wolf, half dead himself. We ate again and lived.

"Meantime the weight upon my shoulders, the little boy whom I carried most of the time, had grown lighter and lighter. I tried to keep him alive. I rubbed him when he was blue with cold and fed him with the few roots that I found, a nut here and there, that had frozen and dried, a leaf from under the snow, at last with the meat of the wolf. It was too late. One day he slipped from my shoulders, I caught him in my arms, and when it was dark I stole away and buried him under the snow."

Kateri was trembling all over now, her eyes wide with

terror. Marie Thérèse hurried on to the end of her story:

"In the winter of 1675 eleven of us had gone to the forest. It was midwinter, the beginning of 1676 when four of us, more dead than alive, staggered into Laprairie de la Madeleine. The mission was still there; it was only in the fall of the same year that it moved here to Caughnawaga.

"The people of the village scarcely knew me. When first I walked the familiar streets again my arms, my legs, seemed no longer to belong to me. From within I was pushing, pushing some weight that had taken the life out of me. I went to the Blackrobe and confessed my sins; but I am impulsive and pleasure loving, Kateri, and I postponed the complete reform of my life, and the penance."

As the story ended both were in tears. "We shall do penance together," Kateri whispered. For a while longer they sat at the foot of the cross and looked out over the swift current of the river. No further word passed between them.

CHAPTER 26 It was June, the month of the strawberry on the St. Lawrence, when the days were sunny and long, and wild cherries glowed in the woods. The seed, blessed for the last time in the small bark chapel, was bursting into life in the softened earth. The church was finished and at the next feast, that of the harvest, the first fruits would be lying upon the new altar. The whitefish, which the Indians called the deer of the water, were swimming swiftly upstream against the rapids and into the nets of the fishermen.

Tekakwitha loved to watch them when she went with Onas to fish; for they could catch them only at the foot of the last leap or sault where they were always found in an attitude of ascending the falls.

"You are like the deer of the water, my Kateri," laughed Marie Thérèse who often went with them, "you swim swiftly upstream; but you are wiser, you never swim into the net."

Kateri laughed in return. "I prefer the rapids to the net." The Fire Fishing also was something new to Kateri. To see lights moving over the water at night, carried in invisible canoes, fascinated her. An Indian sitting in the prow held the torch while another paddled in the stern. The fish, attracted by the light, would come to the surface to be speared and thrown into the boat. In the interplay of darkness and light Kateri, watching, found new thoughts to think and new patterns to weave into her wampum.

She and Marie Thérèse had become inseparable. They went to the fields and to the forest together; they worked and prayed together and told one another their secrets. Each seemed to supply the need of the other. Kateri, so long accustomed to the seclusion of her inner life, shared it willingly and warmly with this understanding friend, who in turn enriched her solitude with the fuller human experience that comes when two people can be together and yet really alone.

"I am glad that those two have found one another," Father Cholenec said to Father Chauchetière one day, seeing them down at the river in animated conversation.

"It is a spiritual friendship, therefore secure," Father Chauchetière replied, "and it is humanly wholesome. Anastasia has up to now been Kateri's only intimate companion. She needs a friend who is closer to her own age. Marie Thérèse is strong and buoyant. She will be good for Kateri."

"And Kateri," said Father Cholenec, "will have a calming influence on Marie Thérèse, and make her more stable."

One sunlit morning toward the end of June, Kateri and Marie Thérèse with a party of other Indians paddled out below the great rapid into the river where it widens to a lake. The two canoes were filled with handiwork which they were taking to Ville Marie, later to be Montreal, for barter, and Kateri's wampum belts, her deerskin collars and embroidered moccasins were their finest wares. This however was of little moment to Kateri in the enthusiasm of her first journey to Ville Marie, and her eyes struggled through the sunlight to gather their first impressions of the unfolding landscape.

Though the southern shore swung into a wide curve as they left Caughnawaga or the Sault, they could still see the tall wooden cross at the margin of the river and the wild little island, the Isle-aux-Hérons, rising like a patch of forest in the swirling foam of the rapids. Prairies stretched southward toward Lake Champlain and Mount Royal towered in the North as they passed the small French settlement with the Jesuit chapel at Laprairie and approached the Isle St. Paul. When they rounded the island and paddled toward the northern shore they saw the first French fort, built by the Sieur de Maisonneuve at the mouth of a small stream. The second fort stood on higher ground with the great French guns pointing toward the river. As the canoes passed below them Kateri looked up. She had seen cannon once before and a lurid picture leaped into her memory: a headlong flight before de Tracy's oncoming army, the Mohawk Valley in flames, the wearisome journey home to a ruined village. Finally, the cross of the Blackrobe!

They landed at the rear of a group of fortified buildings that fronted St. Paul's Street, the principal thoroughfare of the town. Marie Thérèse had seen this French settlement that was destined to grow into a great city, and she enjoyed the wonderment on Tekakwitha's face. Every house on the island of Montreal was built for defense and a chain of redoubts joined the neighboring farms to the town. High walls and outlying defenses surrounded not only the governor's mansion, but mills and brewery as well, also the hospital or Hôtel-Dieu and the principal residences. The buildings were so placed that a cross fire from them and from the first fort could be conducted in such a way that the colonists were protected against an attack from the Indians. Kateri, who loved her adopted country and never ceased being grateful for the shelter that it was giving her, felt a twinge of pain at this reminder of the continual menace that her people had been to its peace.

The gallant Maisonneuve, at the time of Tekakwitha's visit, had been recalled to France and de Courcelle was his successor. For the first time she saw all around her the symbols of another civilization, hints of a foreign history, and a manner of life totally different from her own. The other Indians of the party quickly made their way to the market place on St. Paul's Street and set out their goods for display; but Marie Thérèse had other plans for Kateri's first visit to Ville Marie.

They lingered along St. Paul's Street, looking at the rectangular houses all built in the same style, either of wood, piece upon piece, or of rounded stones held together with cement, and covered with a steep roof. Kateri was amazed at the two skylights of the garret, at the door between two windows in the front, so different from the bearskin curtain and the chimney window of the long house. The weather was not hot, but some of the colonists had already exchanged their usual woolen coats with girdle and "capot" for their summer attire of a cooler shirt and a broad-brimmed hat. The latter recalled to Kateri her childish awe at the enormous hats worn by the Dutch. Her life in the Mohawk Valley lay far behind her; but during these awakening days it was constantly rising before her, chiefly by way of contrast. She was gathering impressions of which she did not know even the name. Horizons of river and forest were widening to the preliminary beat of a city and to the ways of human beings who wore strange garments, spoke a different language, and built wondrous houses that let the light shine in.

Kateri and Marie Thérèse had reached St. Joseph's Street at the corner of St. Paul's, where they paused.

"If we go up this way," said Marie Thérèse indicating the slope up St. Joseph's Street, "we shall come to a square where they have laid stones for a mighty church like the white man builds beyond the Great Water."

Already the Sulpicians and the colonists had laid the foundations for the envisioned church, twin-towered Notre Dame.

"But what place is this?" asked Kateri; for they were standing in front of some chapel with a small cross above the entrance.

"This is a hospital," said Marie Thérèse. "The French call it Hôtel-Dieu."

"What is a hospital?" asked Kateri, impressed by Marie Thérèse's superior knowledge.

"A place where they gather all the sick and take care of them."

Kateri looked admiringly up at her guide. "Who takes care of them?" she asked, almost timidly.

"A number of white squaws who live together, dress alike in a special costume, never marry, and spend their lives praying and doing good," Marie Thérèse explained. Kateri was awe-struck at this revelation. Her companion led the way into the chapel.

They saw no one; but from behind a wooden grille they heard the Sisters chanting office. This was like another world to Kateri. She dropped to her knees and the rapture of a new prayer was on her face. She did not understand why the

Sisters were hidden; but it was beautiful, to pray and sing
to Rawenniio away from all the world.

Again Marie Thérèse took the lead, and at the heavy
wooden door facing St. Paul's Street, they obtained permission to visit the hospital. The door opened into a small
building behind which several other buildings, mostly of
wood, stood in an enclosure surrounded by a high stockade.
Everything was primitive, but to Kateri it was a wonderland.
In one corner she saw a little bakery, in another a garden.

"This is where Soeur de Bresoles cultivates her medicinal
plants to make drugs," the Sister Portress explained in Iroquois. "I shall leave you with her; she will show you
everything."

Soeur de Bresoles rose from her knees with a little trowel
in her hand, and came to meet them with a smile of welcome.
These two had not come from idle curiosity. This she could
see. She noted at once their intelligent interest in all that
she showed them. She told them all that she could, especially about the heroic Mademoiselle Jeanne Manse who,
through the charity of a wealthy lady in Paris, had come from
France and founded this hospital. Mademoiselle Manse herself had nursed the sick, both colonists and Indians, until the
Sisters came from France. She continued to live near them
and to manage everything for them until her death, and that
was only five years ago, Soeur de Bresoles said.

With great enthusiasm the Sister told of the courage and
the charity of this valiant woman who was one of the great
influences and supports of the colony during the heroic years
of its beginning. She was part of those early days in the
history of America, when a burning ideal made its way into
a wilderness. Amid a turmoil of warring tribes and races

parallel for a Mohawk girl in her pursuit of peace and holiness.

Kateri and Marie Thérèse had just left the Hôtel-Dieu and crossed to the opposite side where they were looking with curiosity at a large stone building, when they saw an energetic little figure in black approaching them. She wore a pointed white collar and the edges of a white cap showed from under what was either a short veil worn like a hood, or a large black kerchief knotted loosely below the chin. An empty basket was swinging from her arm.

"Good afternoon, dear children," she said in fluent Iroquois. "Did you come from the mission at Caughnawaga?" Her brown eyes were bright and laughing. Her whole face smiled and the Indian girls smiled with her.

"You must come in with me and stay as long as you are in Ville Marie. You must give me all the news of the mission. I am Sister Marguerite Bourgeoys."

Her friendliness was infectious and they felt at ease with her.

At the first sight of a school in action Kateri held her breath, and even the more experienced Marie Thérèse was speechless, as children of the forest would be. The Sisters were conducting their classes. Indian girls were among the Canadians, and Kateri was amazed to see that they could read, write, and spin. They behaved exactly like the demure little French girls. Except for their features and sometimes their coloring, they could scarcely be distinguished from them; for the complexion of the Mohawks frequently differs little from that of the Latins.

Most of the Indian girls were much younger than Kateri, though one of them, Attontinon, an Onondaga girl called Mary Barbara since her baptism, was more nearly of her age.

This girl wanted to enter the community; but was as yet too recent a convert to be admitted. During these days Marie Thérèse and Kateri learned many things about the Sisters, their daily duties, their lives of prayer and service, and that they remained unmarried and separated from the world.

That Marguerite Bourgeoys was a leading spirit in Ville Marie, was evident. Marie Thérèse and Kateri were troubled to see how continuously she spent herself, and that she did it always with the same joyousness of spirit. The Sisters taught the day pupils free of charge and during the remaining hours at their disposal, worked to support themselves. Sister Bourgeoys, however, was careful to tell the Indian girls that the King of France was specially interested in them, since he allowed her a certain sum every year for the support of the Indian pupils.

Most of them had gone to the newly established mission on the near side of Mount Royal, where their number was increasing daily. One of the Sulpicians instructed the boys and two Sisters of the Congregation of Notre Dame, as Marguerite Bourgeoys called her community, taught the girls. Sister Bourgeoys soon perceived that her two guests from Caughnawaga were unusual even among so fervent a group as the Christians of the Praying Castle. She was the more eager therefore, that they see the new mission and she herself with Attontinon, or Mary Barbara, found time to take them.

The buildings of Ville Marie extended from the river to St. Jacques' Street; and the road beyond, to the mission at Mount Royal was a lonely one. It led past a fortified farm, Saint Gabriel, which belonged to the Sulpicians and where one of their priests was tomahawked in 1661; but there had been many such occurrences in the early days of Ville Marie. Sister Bourgeoys, however, was not afraid of lonely places.

Besides, it was some time since she had visited her little charge Marie Thérèse Gannensagwas.

"The child has your name," she told Marie Thérèse, and as they walked toward the mountain she continued to speak of the little girl, now eleven years old, who had come from the land of the Senecas some years ago with her old grandfather. He was a Christian and had been baptized in the Huron country by the great Blackrobe, Father Brébeuf. Governor de Courcelle adopted Gannensagwas and placed her in charge of Marguerite Bourgeoys.

The two towers of the old fort still remain as a memory of the mission and stand within the entrance to the grounds of the Sulpician seminary in the present city of Montreal. A tablet in one of the towers has kept the name of Marie Thérèse Gannensagwas alive for many years. Probably less than ten years after Kateri Tekakwitha's visit to Ville Marie the little Seneca entered the community of Marguerite Bourgeoys, became a teacher of the Indians and has the distinction of being the first Indian to become a Sister.

The Caughnawaga Indians, meantime, had finished their bartering, and before leaving they all went together to visit the stone chapel of Bon Secours just completed, and at that time a short distance beyond the town. They were eager to see the small gold statue that Marguerite Bourgeoys had brought from France. It stood above the Tabernacle and they prayed before it with enraptured eyes.

Kateri was even more silent than usual as the canoes slipped out of the shadow of the guns and into the open river. Ville Marie had given her much during her three days there. Something had awakened within her, something that she had felt, but was now beginning to understand. She had no desire to stay in the little city. She would take what it had given her, back to the forest and into the lonely places where she felt at home. All that she had seen at Hôtel-Dieu, at the convent of Marguerite Bourgeoys, the lives of the Sisters, their vows, their motivation, had gone deeply into her soul. If she entertained any desire of entering their communities, she gave no sign; but she grasped the essential quality of the life that they led and she took it home with her, into her own life in its most intimate workings.

Kateri and Marie Thérèse had resolved never to separate and to share their thoughts and desires in a united effort to draw closer to God and to deepen their love for Him. As soon as they were alone again at the foot of the cross on the riverbank, they began to exchange confidences. Both had been indelibly impressed by the life of the Sisters in Montreal. They had caught an inkling of disciplines, of iron girdles, of hair shirts; but most important of all, they had learned of the vow by which the Sisters consecrated their virginity to God. With the regulated life of the convent as an example, they determined to direct their lives upon similar lines.

As a fundamental point they resolved never to marry and every day they performed some act of devotion adapted to their particular aims.

"I think it would be better," Marie Thérèse suggested, "if we had a third person with us, some other Christian girl from whom we could learn all that we want to know."

"Perhaps you are right," Kateri said after a thoughtful moment or two.

"I know someone," said Marie Thérèse, "who seems to be the very one that we need. Her name is Marie Skarichions. She is older than we and has lived for a long time in Quebec at the Mission of Our Lady of Lorette which is conducted on the same plan as our mission."

As a result the three met at the foot of the cross to talk things over. Marie, the new companion, expressed her desire to join them and advised that they adopt the rule of the religious with whom she had become acquainted at the hospital in Quebec. They should dress alike, never separate, and if possible occupy the same lodge.

"Where shall we go to live?" Marie Thérèse asked.

Kateri meantime had been looking steadily out over the water toward the Island of the Herons. In a flash they caught her thought.

"There it is!" they exclaimed. "Just the place for our little long house convent. There no one will disturb us."

Full of enthusiasm they made their plans for a rule of life, a bare little cabin, an oratory with a cross out under the trees. It was going to be very beautiful.

"But we must be sure," said Kateri, "that it is God's will. One of us must go to Father Frémin and ask his advice, so that we do nothing contrary to obedience."

"You go, Marie Thérèse," Marie Skarichions urged.

The Oneida went, and she told Father Frémin of the association that they had formed; but that they would do nothing without his consent. The missionary laughed quietly and kindly.

"All of you are still too young in the Faith, my child, for such an undertaking," he began. "Besides, Heron Island is so far from the village that all the young people on their way to and from Ville Marie will be stopping at your cabin. You would seldom be alone."

When Marie Thérèse brought the message to her companions all three agreed that the priest was right and they abandoned the idea at once.

CHAPTER **28** "Kateri dear," her adopted sister, Ennita, called on a sunny morning in early July when the light was too bright for Kateri to work in the field, "I have been wanting to talk to you and this is a good chance. We are alone. Come, sit down for a few minutes."

Without the slightest foreboding Kateri sat down on the mat beside Ennita. "It must be admitted, Kateri, my dear sister," she began, "that you have a great obligation to our Lord for having brought both you and us from our miserable country, and for leading you to the Sault where you can work for your salvation in peace of mind, without anything to trouble your devotion. If you are happy to be here, I am not less happy to see you here with us. Increase this happiness by your wise conduct, which will draw on you the esteem and approbation of the whole village."

Kateri gave her a puzzled look.

"There is just one thing," Ennita continued gently, "which you can do to make me entirely pleased with you, and which will make you yourself perfectly happy — that is to think seriously of establishing yourself by a good, sound marriage."

A startled look leaped into Kateri's eyes and her breath came more quickly. Ennita smiled ingratiatingly; but gave her sister no chance to interrupt.

"This is the course followed by all the girls here," she continued. "You are of a marriageable age, and you need it, even as the others, to withdraw you from the occasions of sin and to supply you with the necessities of life. It is not because it is not a pleasure for your brother-in-law and myself to provide for you, as we have done heretofore, but you know that he is getting old and we have a large family, so that if anything should happen to us and we could not help you, where would you look for aid?" At this Ennita came closer and placed her hand over Kateri's, "Believe me, my dear sister, you should place yourself as soon as possible beyond the danger of the pains of poverty for the good of both your soul and body, and think seriously of how to avoid them while you are able to do so easily, and with such advantage for yourself and for your whole family who desire it."

Kateri loved and respected her sister; for this reason she did not show the pain that had gathered force with every argument that Ennita advanced in this carefully prepared piece of Iroquois eloquence. Kateri, whose work was more than adequate for her support, gave no show of offense at the implication that her family had to provide for her. She even tried to smile when she said: "Thank you, Ennita, for your advice. The matter is of such importance that I must take time to think it over."

This resourceful reply postponed the issue and gave Tekakwitha an opportunity to go at once to tell her director, Father Cholenec.

"Kateri," he said, looking at her intently, "in this matter you are the judge. It depends upon you alone; but think well, for it is a concern of great moment."

"Ah! my Father," she said without the slightest hesitation, "I will not marry. I will not marry. I have the greatest aversion to marriage. The thing is impossible."

It was the dark cry of negation again, emerging from the unplumbed depths of the self that she was, long ago in the Mohawk Valley, when she was growing out of her childhood. In order to sound those depths Father Cholenec brought her attention to the reasons with which her sister had confronted her.

"The thought of poverty does not frighten me," Kateri said. "My work will always supply the food that I require, and a few rags are sufficient to cover me."

Father Cholenec, completely satisfied, sent her home with the assurance that she was doing the right thing. She had not as yet told him all. She had shown him the foundations as they were, even in the old pagan days before Christianity had worked upon them, before Love had built its solitary citadel. With keen intuition she had always suspected that there were practices of the Christian life over and above those required at the mission, that were still hidden from her. The Blackrobes had tempered their demands to the limited capabilities of their neophytes. But she had been to Ville Marie. For the first time the spiritual world of Europe had touched the orbit of her own sphere as with a flash of light. She had learned something of the Evangelical Counsels and seen them in action among the religious of Ville Marie. She had considered these things carefully with Marie Thérèse, and together they had agreed never to marry, she dedicating her virginity and Marie Thérèse her perpetual widowhood to God. They had kept this decision secret and decided to speak of it only if absolutely necessary.

Because of Ennita's insistence, the time had come. Kateri hesitated to let her know that the matter was already settled; but her sister, thinking that sufficient time had passed, pressed her for her decision. In the hope of putting an end, once and for all, to this annoyance, Kateri said that she had renounced marriage, and asked to be permitted to live as she was.

"As for the rest," she added, "I have enough clothes for a long time and I'll work to support myself so as not to be a burden to you, dear Ennita, or to anyone in the village."

"My sister," Ennita exclaimed, deeply moved, "how did you form such a strange resolution? Have you ever seen or heard tell of such a thing among the Mohawk girls, or even in all the Iroquois family? Where did you get this strange idea? Can you not see that you expose yourself to the derision of men and the temptations of the devil?" Ennita's words gathered momentum as she grew more and more excited. "Can you expect to accomplish what no girl among us has ever done? Forget these thoughts, my dear sister; do not trust your own strength, but follow the custom of the other girls." Her voice shook as she finished.

"I am not afraid of the jeers of men so long as I am doing nothing wrong," Kateri replied without any display of emotion, "and I hope that God will give me the necessary strength to overcome any temptation of the devil that may threaten me. Dear sister, my resolution has already been taken. Please do not speak of it any more."

Ennita did not dare to allude to it again; but she told Anastasia who, as mistress of the lodge, occupied the place of a mother to both of them, and she presented her arguments so convincingly that she won Anastasia to her point of view. The two women were honestly disturbed. Both of them were devout Christians and eager to please God as best they could; but an idea like Kateri's was utterly strange even to them. There was no precedent and it seemed not only difficult, but morally impossible; for it was a manner of life totally opposed to that of the Indian.

Anastasia was wise. After weighing all the reasons that Ennita had given, she feared that Kateri had acted on impulse and that in time she would regret a resolution taken so lightly. She therefore did everything in her power to deter her from so strange a purpose. Kateri was amiable as always; but firm. Anastasia failed as Ennita had; but she did not give up. She was so persistent that Kateri finally said with a determination that ended all argument: "I do not wish to hear anything more on the subject."

Anastasia was shocked at such resistance, which she mistook for obstinacy. She knew of the suffering that Kateri was made to endure for the same cause in the Mohawk Valley, and she had felt deeply sorry for her; but here it was different. This was a Christian village. Any young brave of the mission would be happy to find so virtuous a wife, and Kateri could surely choose a suitable husband from among them. Anastasia decided to go to the priest at once and complain of Kateri. Surely he would have some influence over her.

Kateri on her part lost no time in going again to Father Cholenec. She told him that her foster mother and her sister left her no peace, that they insisted upon her marrying and she found it impossible to obey them. Father Cholenec saw that she was suffering intensely and that he must help her settle the matter.

"Take three more days to consider the subject, my child," he said kindly, "pray earnestly and recommend your difficulty to our Lord, then follow closely whatever He inspires you to do. Remember that you are your own mistress, and in an affair of this kind the decision rests with you. I shall pray with you."

Kateri agreed; but it took her only a few moments to think about a choice that she had made long ago, and she returned almost immediately after she had left.

"My Father," she said, and her manner was shy and embarrassed, "I cannot live longer in a state of indecision."

Then she disclosed the whole of her secret. She had renounced marriage in order to have only Jesus Christ for her Spouse, and she would consider herself happy to live in poverty and misery for the sake of His love.

Father Cholenec had been careful not to direct Kateri in this matter, since among the Indians such an ideal had seemed too difficult at this stage in their spiritual development. Therefore he preferred to let God influence His creature directly, firm in the belief that all would turn out well and that reassuring evidences would not be wanting. After Kateri's avowal a look of relief, then of wonderment passed over Father Cholenec's face. Almost imperceptibly he nodded as though in unison with some inner affirmation.

"Kateri," he said quietly, "I am sure that our Lord is pleased with your resolution. Continue in it with the same firmness and fervor with which you have begun. I will defend you; have no fear. Neither I nor the other Fathers will ever abandon you or allow you to want for anything."

"Oh! Father! Thank you! Thank you!"

The tenseness vanished from her face. The peace and joy of a great release replaced it. The missionary saw it and his mind was at rest.

No sooner had Tekakwitha left than Anastasia came, lamenting that the girl was of marriageable age and yet had refused to take a husband.

"I am surprised, Anastasia," Father Cholenec answered coldly, "that you are tormenting her about a matter that deserves so much praise, and that you who have been a Christian for so many years have not opened your eyes to

the beauty and merit of a life such as she wishes to lead."
Anastasia's eyes dropped.

Father Cholenec continued inexorably, "You should admire
her the more and feel honored because God has chosen a
young girl from your cabin to show the Indians what virginity is. They know nothing of this virtue which makes
men like the angels, and she will be the first example among
them of the life that even the Blessed Mother chose." Anastasia's head was bowed in shame and sorrow. For her it was
the awakening from a deep sleep and she understood at once.
She blamed herself without mercy and began to look upon her
young charge as a saint. Thereafter she not only encouraged
her as having chosen the better part, but she convinced
Ennita of it. The persecution was over. For Kateri it had been
even more painful than what she had endured in the Mohawk
Valley because it was more plausible, and because of the
Christian character of the ones who had inflicted it upon her.

Late that evening after the disturbances of the day were
over, Father Cholenec and Father Chauchetière sat together
in the darkness of their cabin. Both agreed that Kateri's
arrival and her subsequent conduct had been a turning point
in the spiritual life of the mission.

"I should not have believed it possible in this country which
is still more or less the North American wilderness," said
Father Cholenec.

"Not altogether a wilderness," mused Father Chauchetière,
"where such a thing can happen."

"We are thinking of the usual achievements of men,"
Father Cholenec resumed. "Here we are dealing with God.
I was gravely puzzled at first and wanted to say nothing to
determine Kateri in this delicate matter. I was uncertain as to
the human causes that may have lain at the base of a mere

weakened, would have to suffer the more cruelly, she knew.

"You are sparing me, Marie Thérèse," Kateri cried out. "Strike harder."

Marie Thérèse saw that the third stroke had already drawn blood; nevertheless she had to continue in order to satisfy Kateri, who would like to have atoned for the sins of all the Mohawks.

"It is my turn. Please, Kateri, it is enough," Marie Thérèse insisted. She knelt and bared her own strong shoulders. Kateri staggered to her feet, smiling to hide her fatigue. She thanked Marie Thérèse and lifted her aching arms that could do only with the greatest difficulty, all that was demanded of them.

Joyously, when all was over they went to the chapel together, their shoulders covered with blood. No one knew. They never found their prayers so short, nor had they ever been happier. In their insatiable enthusiasm for expiation they looked for a permanent place to which they could resort for their penances and found it in a deserted cabin which the owner, a Frenchman living at Laprairie, had left open. It stood in the center of the cemetery and was therefore a place of perfect seclusion.

The two friends, remaining in perfect accord, inspired one another to the utmost capabilities of each. Through Marie Thérèse, Kateri's words have been preserved for us, revealing the spirit with which she entered into this voluntary punishment. Occasionally, when the self-inflicted chastisement was nearing its end, she would disclose what was in her heart and cry out: "My Jesus, I must suffer for Thee; I love Thee, but I have offended Thee. It is to satisfy Thy justice that I am here."

Sometimes she could not speak and her eyes filled with

tears. To her the Passion of Christ and sin were living realities and therefore the inexhaustible sources of her thirst for suffering. "I am deeply affected by the three nails which fastened our Lord to the cross," she would say, "they are but a symbol of my sins."

The sins which so afflicted her were what she called her laxness of life before baptism when she did not resist those who forced her to work on Sundays and holydays, and did not prefer to suffer martyrdom, and the fact that she had often feared death more than sin.

A year of secret penance passed. It was the year that Father Frémin spent in France. This, according to Father Chauchetière, was a possible reason why Kateri and Marie Thérèse spoke to no one of what they were doing.

It is interesting in the light of a later day, a light grown dim, perhaps, by too many centuries of civilization, to adjust the vision to an earlier age or else to focus it upon a remote corner of the world while a regenerating spirit is blowing fresh upon a primitive people. This may in a measure help us to understand the austerities of Kateri Tekakwitha. On the other hand, though externals may differ and modes of expression vary according to time, place, and other circumstances, there is a resemblance that is startling, among all the superlative lovers of Christ Crucified. In any love worthy of the name, there is a growing disregard of self on the part of the lover, a tendency to give not merely an extraneous gift, but something of the self. The name of this kind of gift is suffering. The test of this kind of love is sacrifice. This has been done for many a lesser cause than the pure love of God and His crucified Christ. But when this supreme motive actuates the souls of men and divine love runs like a living fire through the holy ones of the earth, they burn with the desire for sacrifice that finds its expression in penance, penance for personal sin and for the sins of the world.

Thus Kateri, innocent though she was, and frail of body, fasted, labored, scourged herself. She walked barefoot over the jagged ice of a pond in the woods, during the winter hunt, and many times through the snow. In frozen February, as an act of love to our Lady for the Feast of the Purification, she prayed the rosary several times while walking through the field, buried to the waist in snow. But she did these things only when she thought herself unobserved.

"What do you consider the severest form of torture?" she asked Anastasia one day.

"Fire," the latter replied.

Forthwith Kateri, when no one saw her, put a burning brand to her feet and legs up to the knees. Then, although it was night, she walked to the chapel and offered this new sacrifice of herself to our Lord. On another occasion Marie Thérèse expressed her intention of branding her foot as one did to slaves, thus declaring herself a slave of Jesus Christ. This Kateri also wished to do; but Marie Thérèse, at the thought of the ember burning her flesh, feared that she would not be brave enough to endure it. She meant to do it through the length of a Hail Mary which, in the Iroquois tongue, is longer than in English; but she had to give up. Kateri persevered, and when Marie Thérèse visited her the next day she noticed a deep mark in her foot, which must have caused her an agony of pain.

To an ease-loving age these things may seem repellent. Penance for its own sake would not attract even the saints, and certainly it fails in its remedial purpose if there be any trace of vainglory in it. In the motivation lies the secret. If it be love, there is beauty in it; and if there be folly in the extreme expression of love, it is the folly of heroism.

As to Kateri, several circumstances must be considered. Two strong influences worked upon her. Anastasia's teaching had been severe, and Marie Thérèse had led a sinful life that needed penance. Furthermore she was an Indian and a Mohawk. Among the Indian nations none more than the Iroquois, and among the Iroquois none more than the Mohawks were masters in the art of torture. They knew equally well how to give and how to endure it. No one, more than an Iroquois, scorned the weakling and admired even an enemy who could bear the most grueling pain and give no sign that he suffered. It was they who had eaten the heart of Brébeuf that they might be filled with his courage.

But the intensity of Tekakwitha's courage came from a different source and when we sift her passion for penance down to its essential quality we find it free from any ambition for personal heroism, and we see the beauty of a love that is selfless lying like a mantle over its austerity. We see furthermore that in comparison with the severity of the penances that many of the Christian Indians performed, Kateri's mortifications appear in a more moderate light, tempered as they were by the humility of a perfect obedience. Of the spirit that animated the mission of the Sault Father Cholenec writes: "It was a new church possessed of extraordinary graces and the holiness which prevailed there was worthy of the early Church." "The Iroquois," he continues, "had become strongly attached to the Church, and these ardent and brave neophytes had conceived such sorrow and shame for the sins of their past lives that even though they had been effaced by baptism, they still performed great penances for them."

It is not unusual, for instance, to hear of some who, several times a week, chastised their bodies until they bled, and of others who while gathering firewood wore iron bands for entire days. Ice and snow also provided frequent opportunities for penance. Some rolled in the snow in severest winter weather or, having broken the ice with hatchets stood up to the neck in pools and rivers. One woman did this while in the forest on three successive nights and when she returned to the cabin, lest others become aware of her penance, she did not go near the fire, but lay down on her mat and spent the rest of the night wrapped in a coat of ice.

We find a still more violent example in a woman named Anne, the wife of a certain Etienne who was a devout and well-known Christian of the mission. This Anne, not content with plunging herself into the icy river, submerged also her three-year-old daughter and pulled her out half dead. When the missionary learned of it he reprimanded her severely and questioned her as to the motives that led to so pitiless an action. She answered in good faith that she feared that when the child grew older she would grow lax and fall into sin. Therefore she had forced her to do penance in advance.

There was a tendency in the Indian to match the ferocity of the sins of the nation with a ferocity of expiation. Against this background Tekakwitha stands, with nothing of ferocity in her, yet surpassing all, even of that ardent company, in holiness of life. Like an arrow flying straight to its target, she loved with the wholeness of her nature, warmly, deeply, understandingly. No gift was too great to give to God and the proof of her love was sacrifice. She needed but to look at the Crucifix to understand this and to realize simply and in her own complete way, what sin had done. With this deepened penetration added to all that she had seen of sin in some of its most hideous manifestations, the result was inevitable. We see austerities, but we see also profound peace and an ever growing love. The Christian Faith had shown her something that she, handicapped as she was, could do, and she did it fully. Her disregard for her ailing body had nothing of the fanatic in it. In her it was the simple outcome of a sense of values. She appreciated her soul and would not permit the lesser thing to hamper the functioning of the greater.

After the summer was over, Father Cholenec suggested that she go to the woods for the winter hunt; but she would not hear of it.

"It will help to restore your health," he said. "You will suffer for want of nourishment if you remain in the village, and the winter is long." Kateri laughed gaily for a moment; but her eyes pleaded as she said:

"Ah! my Father; it is true that the body fares well in the woods, but the soul languishes there and dies of hunger, whereas in the village, the body suffers a little from not being so well nourished, but the soul, being close to our Lord finds entire satisfaction. Therefore I abandon this miserable body to hunger and any other misery, that my soul may be content and have its usual nourishment."

It happened as she said; the body suffered, but the soul was at peace and the cheerfulness which was an inseparable part of her being, increased rather than diminished. This quality was put to the test one day while Kateri and Marie Thérèse were returning from the field. Both carried large bundles of wood and Kateri was wearing an iron girdle with long spikes securely hidden under her tunic. While coming down a hill she slipped and fell on the ice. Marie Thérèse, through whom the incident came to light, dropped her bundle, hurried to help her companion, and found that the fall had forced the spikes well into the flesh. Kateri laughed, would not let her friend carry the wood, but picked up her bundle and returned to her cabin as cheerily as though nothing had happened. No further evidence is needed not only of Kateri's constant spirit of penance, but of a sister spirit of cheerfulness and a sense of humor that was genuine.

CHAPTER 30 On the morning of
March 25 of the year 1679, patches of field were still white
with untrodden snow and islands of breaking ice floated
heavily on the St. Lawrence; but the stir of spring was in
the air and in the thawing earth. The new bell from France
had arrived in exchange for the long collected beaver furs,
and all four bells were ringing together for our Lady's An-
nunciation. The chapel was crowded for the eight o'clock
Mass and a slender figure wrapped in a long blue shawl was
kneeling motionless, not far from the communion rail. As
always when at prayer, Kateri was oblivious of everything
around her; but today a new light burned in her eyes, and
her whole face glowed in its radiance. This was the day
dedicated to her vow of virginity, the culmination of years
of inner growing toward an ideal that was supernatural.

Not long after her arrival at the Sault when marriage was
again suggested to her and Father Frémin told her that she
was free either to marry or not, she had resolved to lead a
life of virginity. She had kept this intention secret until the
persistence of those who were trying to urge her into marriage forced her to disclose it. And now but one thing remained. She wanted to make her decision final, irrevocable,
and protected by the sacredness of a vow. Father Cholenec
had given his consent at last.

This development was a strange, silent thing in the soul of Kateri. She knew nothing of the virtue of virginity on that strenuous evening when she fled from the marriage rite of the Mohawks and hid among the corn. But Christianity had penetrated her innermost being and filled its deep-dug channels. In place of a turning away from some unloved objective, there was now a turning toward something of which Christianity had given her the name. She was the hart that pants for cooling springs, and the springs of her desire lay in high and hidden places.

A few moments after she received Holy Communion on this the very day commemorating Mary's tremendous words of surrender, this daughter of the Mohawks, renouncing forever the human happiness of marriage, chose Christ alone for her Spouse, making to God the same complete dedication that Christ's Mother had made, also against the traditions of her race. It was to honor Mary that Kateri united with her vow a double consecration, offering herself first of all to Christ, then to His Blessed Mother. With this act the greatest desire of her life was fulfilled. She no longer belonged to herself nor did she seem any longer to belong to this world.

CHAPTER 31 Father Cholenec contin-
ued to watch Kateri Tekakwitha closely. He had come from
the European world where sanctity was an old, old story.
His native France had a long spiritual tradition by which
one might learn to evaluate holiness of life. He had come to
grips with the wilderness and knew what to expect of it. It
was he who spoke of Kateri as "the miracle of our forests."
He saw that the otherworldliness that had grown more and
more into her character did not alienate the people from her.
She walked her simple way among them as before, helping
with the sick, caring for children, performing in so far as
she was able any work of charity that offered itself. The
French as well as the Indians were aware of a certain in-
describable quality about her that attracted them. In her,
womanhood had fulfilled its destiny of surrender in its most
selfless, its supernatural form; yet she lost none of her natural,
womanly charm. All who came into association with her
were drawn to her, not by the things that she did, but by
the person that she was.

The candle was burning low; while the light that consumed it was mounting steadily to a more intense flame.
Kateri was throwing more and more fuel into the fire of
her love. So urgent and unrelenting was the striving of the
spirit toward an increasingly profound union with God, that

it exhausted her physical forces and during the succeeding summer she became seriously ill and narrowly escaped with her life. Nevertheless her health was permanently undermined, she was in constant pain, and a low fever induced a languor that she could not dispel. But her devotion continued to the end in the fullness of its ardor. She did not relax in her attendance at morning Masses nor in her frequent visits to the Blessed Sacrament when she would kneel for hours even on the coldest days of winter. Many a time Father Cholenec would find her in the church, her body nearly frozen, and whisper to her:

"Come, my child, and warm yourself at our fire."

She followed him at once; but after a few moments made her escape, saying with her bright smile:

"Thank you, my Father; but I am not cold," and hurrying back to the chapel she would kneel again in the place that she loved. She may not have been aware of the cold; but her weakening body told her that life on earth was nearing its end, and her spirit leaped to the challenge. She must not lose a moment of the time that remained. More and more it became true of her that she knew but two paths from her cabin, one to the chapel, the other to the field.

In the cold of February, Lent came. She was wearing her burden strap and gathering wood again. A blinding snow was falling and the winds were blowing wild, just like they did long ago in the woods of the Mohawk Valley when the fires in the long house were nearly out. Her thoughts were Lenten thoughts, of the Passion of our Lord, and as she stumbled about, gathering stray bits of firewood, she came upon a brier bush with long, sharp thorns protruding through the snow. With avidity she grasped the prickly branches, made a large bundle and hid it among the wood. Heavily it hung upon her back and bore upon the burden strap fastened to her forehead. She had been seeking new ways of sharing the cross of Christ, and an incident in the life of St. Aloysius which Father Cholenec had casually related one day, leaped into her mind and clamored for imitation. No one, not even Anastasia, saw her when she reached the cabin and hastily concealed the brambles under the mat of her lodge seat. When everyone was asleep she strewed the thorns upon her mat, lay down, and covered herself with her blanket. The next morning when she rose, she was spent from a sleepless night upon her bed of thorns; but her heart was singing a joyous hymn of love.

Marie Thérèse came early and they walked to Mass together. All the way Kateri felt her companion's eyes upon her. Nothing escaped Marie Thérèse. She saw that Kateri was weak and worn, that her breath came quickly, and that while her lips smiled, her eyes had pain in them. She saw too that when she prayed, her shoulders seemed to have shrunken and her head drooped as though she held it with difficulty.

"Take more rest, my Kateri," Marie Thérèse counseled on the way home. "Don't feel that you must do everything in one day. Leave something for tomorrow."

Kateri smiled affectionately at her friend: "There will not be many tomorrows, Marie Thérèse." And the light crept back for a moment into her tired eyes.

Every moment was more than ever valuable now. Not a single task was left for tomorrow when she dropped again wearily onto her bed of thorns. The night was long, and darkness hung like a visible presence over her. She thought of her family, the people of her tribe living in the Mohawk Valley.

"This is for them," she whispered brokenly. "Rawenniio have pity. Send Your beautiful light into their darkness!"

The cries of tortured victims were ringing in her ears again. She turned and let the thorns bite into her anew. She thought of the sins of her people, their drunkenness; of the Blackrobes whose blood they had shed. Lower, lower she sank into the bed with her own blood warm upon it. "Rawenniio, forgive them! Let me pay it in love!"

And the slow dawn rose upon her and the cold of the winter morning cut her as she staggered from her mat, fell back, and rose again, bent and shivering, yet with rivers of fever speeding through her veins. She had scarcely lit the fire when Marie Thérèse appeared. Tekakwitha's face was like that of the dead. She greeted her friend with her usual warmth of manner, though she was surprised to see her so early.

Marie Thérèse suspected the truth. This time she would not be put off.

"Tell me, Kateri," she begged, "what are you doing to yourself? Do not keep this secret from me. Anastasia and Ennita believe that your illness has caused this change in you; but I know better." Her quick eye had seen the thorns as Kateri was hiding them, and Kateri confessed it all, telling her friend also that she meant to continue this practice until her death.

"Yes," Marie Thérèse answered, "but do you know that you are offending God by undertaking this sort of excess without the permission of your confessor?"

Kateri looked startled as she always did at the least shadow of wrong. The drastic words had an immediate effect. She would otherwise have kept this act a secret throughout her life; but now she went at once to Father Cholenec and accused herself. Then she related the whole occurrence. Father Cholenec gave no indication that he was struck with admiration at her courage. He reprimanded her for her imprudence and commanded her to throw the thorns into the fire. She did it at once with that utter freedom from attachment to her own will, that made her equally ready to do or not to do a thing as soon as she recognized it as being or not being the will of God.

After this experience Kateri's body, frail and prone to illness since childhood, was nearly at the end of its resistance. It had served its purpose well as an adaptable instrument, aiding, never impeding, a soul of fire in its flight to an eternal destiny. Since it was the time of the winter hunt, those remaining in the village had no means of sustenance other than Indian corn. Kateri's exhausted body grew weaker, and there were days when she could not leave the cabin. As long as possible she walked to church and when she was unable to kneel in her usual way, she rested on a bench. But the time came when she could no longer move without intense pain, and during the concluding two months of her life she had to keep herself in the same position day and night. Not once did she make the slightest complaint. She was united with the suffering Christ and in that divine companionship was happy.

CHAPTER 32

Tekakwitha lay motionless upon her mat. The bowl of sagamite and the small jug of water that Marie Thérèse had placed beside her before she went to work in the field were still untouched although it was midafternoon. While the men were away on the hunt the few women who remained in the village were busy from morning to night in field or forest; therefore the Indians, during this time, had to leave their sick alone all day with only a bowl of sagamite and a little water beside them.

Kateri, although this was her last illness, did not mind spending it for the most part alone. The inner seclusion to which she had withdrawn even when the crowded life of the long house had swirled about her long ago in the Mohawk Valley, had deepened now into her uttermost solitude. A great silence enfolded her. She immersed herself in it and felt at home. The emptiness of noise had gone, the clamoring past with its many voices, the struggles within and without, all was falling from her, leaving a silence of fullness even to overflowing.

As the afternoon wore on sounds of laughter mingled with the stillness, not breaking it, but rather adding to its meaning. The children were coming! Daily one of the Blackrobes came to visit her; but sometimes Father Chauchetière to provide a little diversion for her, brought his little pupils and gave them their religious instruction at her bedside. With them she could enjoy the pictures from the Old and the New Testament with which he always enlivened the lesson.

A stream of sunlight lit the dim cabin as he drew the bearskin curtain aside while the children rushed in and crowded eagerly around her mat. Her eyes, over which the lids drooped more heavily now, lit with pleasure, and she followed the instruction as attentively as ever, trying with difficulty to prop herself upon her elbow to look at the pictures. Instinctively the children hushed their voices; for she had weakened much since they saw her last and her frail form seemed almost a part of the shadows that surrounded her. More quietly than usual they left the cabin after the lesson was over and Father Chauchetière lingered a moment while he blessed her.

On the Monday of Holy Week Father Cholenec saw that all hope of recovery was gone. All the life left in her seemed to be in her smile. Neither weakness nor suffering had dampened the vivacity of her spirit, which remained not only cheerful as always, but gay.

"It is Holy Week," she whispered to the priest. "May I not perform some act of penance in honor of our Lord's Passion? Some little thing, my Father. Perhaps going without food for just a day?"

Father Cholenec shook his head. "God will accept your good intention, my child. You must think of other things now. You have not long to live."

"Oh! My Father!" Though her voice was but little more than a breath, the throb of exuberance was in it.

"Tomorrow," said Father Cholenec, making an effort to keep his voice steady, "we shall bring our Lord to you."

At this added news she found no further words; but the

look of ecstasy lay like a quiet light upon her face.

At the mission it was unprecedented to bring the Blessed Sacrament to a cabin. The sick were usually carried to the church on a plank or some sort of litter; but Kateri was too weak to be moved. Early on Tuesday morning Marie Thérèse came to her. Kateri was radiant with expectancy. She was summoning all her remaining strength to meet our Lord in Holy Communion and to do it as best she could. Marie Thérèse was kneeling beside her and Kateri's hand slipped into hers.

"Do not leave me at this last moment," she begged. Then a look of anxiety brushed the smile away. "I am poor, Marie Thérèse," she said hesitantly, "utterly poor. I have no clothes to wear, and our Lord is coming."

Marie Thérèse hurried away and returned in a few moments with her own deerskin tunic, a pair of new moccasins, and a warm, blue shawl. She had to turn her face away as she dressed her, remembering the beautiful things that Kateri had sewn and embroidered for others, keeping nothing for herself.

Tenderly she covered her with the shawl, then knelt in silence beside her, while Kateri, scarcely breathing, waited. They could hear the little silver bell tinkling its way through the narrow streets. Father Chauchetière accompanied Father Cholenec as he carried the Blessed Sacrament on this extraordinary journey, and all those left in the village followed in procession.

After having received Holy Viaticum Kateri offered herself in final oblation to God and gave voice to profound gratitude for the graces that had been given to her, especially since she had come to the mission. And the silent Indians stood, with awe upon their faces. The shadows were deepening about her eyes. The priest in sudden fear that he was postponing Extreme Unction too long, ran back the whole way to the Church. When he returned she looked up with a reassuring smile.

"There is no need for hurry, Father," she said with an air of such certainty that he decided to defer her anointing to the following morning. On the way home he remembered that at the beginning of her last illness, fully two months ago, one of the Fathers at the mission had expressed his firm conviction that Kateri would die on the Wednesday of Holy Week, the vigil of the two feasts that were especially dear to her, Holy Thursday because of the Blessed Sacrament and Good Friday for the sake of the Passion. This fact, coupled with Kateri's attitude made a deep impression upon Father Cholenec and remained in his mind for many an hour.

As for the Indians, a spirit of reverence was upon them. Throughout the day they came and went, to look at Kateri and to implore her prayers. The priest, mindful of the fact that the words of the dying often exerted a powerful influence upon the living, urged her to exhort some who needed encouragement. She had never been given to many words and had spoken but little during her two years at the mission. Although it was more than ever against her inclination during these last hours of her life, she spoke to a number of people, both privately and in groups, encouraging and inspiring them, leaving with them thoughts that they would never forget, something of her very self. Beyond this, the time between the reception of the Viaticum and Extreme Unction was as one continuous Holy Communion, with her soul trembling on the margins of Eternity.

In the chapel that evening, Father Cholenec leading the prayers noticed that the congregation responded with tense, hushed voices as though anticipating some awesome event. Two members of the Confraternity of the Holy Family had been appointed to keep the night watch at Kateri's bedside. This meant that she was dying. Anne, an older woman accustomed to such vigils, had been chosen, and Madeleine, the youngest member of the confraternity, was selected as her companion.

After evening prayers Madeleine went to speak to Father Cholenec. She stood before him with imploring eyes; but the words would not come.

"What is it, my child?" the priest asked.

"Will you give me permission?" She hesitated.

"Permission for what?" Father Cholenec prompted.

"Permission to go to the woods and do some penance that Kateri may have a happy death?"

For a moment Father Cholenec did not answer; but his glance understood.

"I love her, Father, and she loves me." Madeleine's eyes filled. She was barely twenty-two and in her first fervor.

"You may do it, my child." Father Cholenec, deeply touched, had no more to say.

Kateri, dying, turned on her mat. No one was in the lodge but the elderly woman who was watching with her.

"Anne," she whispered, "please find Madeleine and ask her to come at once." The woman went, and found Madeleine coming out of the woods, walking toward her cabin. For fifteen minutes, hidden among the trees, she had chastised herself in behalf of her friend, until blood flowed freely and Madeleine, in her mute belief that the test of love is sacrifice, was satisfied. She looked up in surprise at sight of the other woman.

"Let them go to the woods. I shall still be alive when they return."

They believed her implicitly and went away satisfied. She would not disappoint them.

She kept her promise also to Marie Thérèse and a few hours later, at ten o'clock, she sent for her. Breathless, Marie Thérèse came running to the bedside of her friend, in time to be with her while she received the sacrament of Extreme Unction. Death came so near, almost as though it would touch her before noon; but it could not. The women had not come home from the woods and she was keeping her word to them. Marie Thérèse was in tears beside her and Kateri, loving her as deeply as she did, drew heavily upon her ebbing strength to speak to her:

"I am leaving you. I am about to die." Her companion's arm was around her and she was bending low, straining to catch every struggling word. Marie Thérèse was trembling; but Kateri was calm.

"Always remember what we have done together since we knew each other," she continued bravely. "Take courage. . . . Never give up mortification. I will love you in heaven. I will pray for you. I will assist you." This was Kateri's best gift to her friend, the assurance of immortality even for human love when rooted in God.

Her voice made its last effort for the loved names of Jesus and Mary, trailed off to a whisper, and was silent. But consciousness remained, and we have Father Chauchetière's word for it, that her face appeared more like that of one in contemplation than the face of one dying. While the subdued voices of the Blackrobes rose and fell in their prayers for the departing soul, slowly the returning women encircled her. They were in time. She waited until all had come, and when the last one dropped to her knees, death came, so gently that she seemed to fall asleep and no one knew that the last moment had passed. It was three o'clock in the afternoon, April 17, 1680, and Kateri Tekakwitha was scarcely twenty-four years old.

A quarter of an hour later, Father Cholenec, still upon his knees, cried out in astonishment. Her face, ravaged by illness and unrelenting austerities, more swarthy, more disfigured than ever, had grown so white, so beautiful, that not a mark was left upon it. Disfigurement had served its lifelong purpose. Now the inner beauty lay revealed and was there for all to see. The wondering Indians came and looked, and their hearts understood the meaning. This was no time for sorrow. With simple faith they kissed her hands and treasured all that had been hers, everything that she had touched, as a sacred relic. A joyousness was in their tears as they stayed with her throughout the night and looked upon her radiant face whose beauty did not change.

The Blackrobes marveled with their people. Never had they seen such transformation as in the face of Kateri.

"It is as though the paradox of death in life and life in death were unfolding before our very eyes," Father Chauchetière said musingly at the end of that eventful Wednesday. "It is because she is dead that she is so beautiful."

"Yes," said Father Cholenec. "Her achievement, glowing with God's grace, will rest as a blessing forever upon our Caughnawaga. Amid the fervor of this mission she has grown to her full spiritual stature. It has contributed much to her sanctification; but now, she in her turn is sanctifying the mission."

Father Chauchetière seized this opening to repeat a suggestion that he had made earlier in the day.

"Father," he began, "can't I persuade you to have her buried in the church? It will deepen the devotion of the Indians."

Father Cholenec shook his head. "I dare not do it, Father. It would be much too unusual a thing. Her grave is ready, a beautiful spot almost on the edge of the St. Lawrence. You will see. The Indians will go there to pray and bring their sick. Pilgrims will come from far and near. I am convinced of it."

The lighted pine knot was nearly out. It had been a long day and a vital one for the Mission of St. Francis Xavier.

On the morning of Holy Thursday two Frenchmen from Prairie de la Madeleine came to attend services at the Sault. They passed Kateri's cabin on the way and noticing a knot of people gathered there, they looked in and saw a girl with a lovely face lying on her mat, apparently asleep.

"Who is the young woman sleeping so peacefully?" they said to one another.

Marie Thérèse heard. "Don't you know her?" she asked. "Kateri Tekakwitha? She is not asleep. She has gone to heaven."

Amazed, the Frenchmen turned back into the lodge, knelt at her feet, and prayed.

"She is too beautiful to bury in the earth, wrapped in a shawl or a beaverskin. We must make a coffin at once to enclose so precious a thing."

Father Cholenec did not know until several years later that the place which he had selected for her burial was exactly on the spot that Kateri herself had designated some time before her last illness. She was in the cemetery with some other women, one of whom laughingly asked her where her grave would be.

"There," she said, pointing to the spot near the margin of the river. And there, unknowing, they buried her at three o'clock on Holy Thursday afternoon.

Father Chauchetière tells that they could not cover her face, such was the pleasure they took in looking upon it. They had never learned from their catechism as much as they learned here. For this reason her face was left uncovered until they laid her in the grave.

"If only I might have seen it!" Anastasia cried out, with Ennita sobbing beside her, home from the hunt, but too late. Anastasia had held Tekakwitha in her arms on the day that she was born, she had seen Kahenta die, and had nursed her stricken fledgling back to life. She recalled her pain upon discovering the little girl's weakened eyes and scarred face. Wrapped in these memories, the tears were running unchecked down her furrowed cheeks. For her Kateri was a child again.

"Little red-winged bird," she said, "your flight is over now, but your wings were swift and strong."

Kateri did not desert her friends. She strewed her favors with a lavish hand upon all who invoked her. The sick were cured, sinners converted, miracles sprang up like flowers in a watered garden. And in that fervent village new fires of love were lit. "Devotion became general," Father Cholenec writes. "The Indians spoke of penances, of self-denial, of renouncing all in order to give all to God, in imitation of Kateri Tekakwitha."

It is long now since Father Chauchetière's wish has partially fulfilled itself. Kateri's bones have been taken from her grave and are exposed for veneration in the sacristy of the Mission of St. Francis Xavier. The Blackrobes are still in charge of their Indian flock and in the Caughnawaga of today the Iroquois continue to speak, sing, and pray in the language that Kateri knew.

The centuries have hewn their changes into the North American continent. Cities have invaded primeval forests and crowded out the trees. The strongholds of the five nations of the Iroquois have disappeared; but in the Christian world Kateri of the Mohawks will keep her race immortally alive. If the human world will pray, she will doubtless work her miracles again upon the stricken earth. What man has taken from the Indian, God has restored a hundredfold. She is His undying gift to the red man and the red man's timeless contribution to America. Whatever else may come or go in epochs yet to come, Kateri Tekakwitha and the story of her life reveals forever the saving grace of an immortal love.